Essays in Biosynthesis and Microbial Development

Presented at the Institute of Microbiology
Rutgers, the State University of New Jersey

Essays in Biosynthesis and Microbial Development

JOHN D. BU'LOCK

Department of Chemistry,
The University of Manchester.

NEW YORK · LONDON · SYDNEY, JOHN WILEY & SONS, INC.

In recognition of the importance of cooperation between chemist and microbiologist the E. R. Squibb Lectures on Chemistry of Microbial Products were established with the support of The Squibb Institute for Medical Research in 1955. The lectures are presented annually in the fall at the Institute of Microbiology, Rutgers, the State University of New Jersey, New Brunswick, New Jersey.

PREFACE

The topics I wish to present here are given as facets of my own interest in the subject of chemical microbiology, but I hope that their interrelation lies somewhat deeper than this. In the first section I have tried to relate some of the "natural products" encountered in our work, substances many would regard as quite unnatural, to a particular type of natural function. A consideration of the role of secondary metabolites in the natural life of microorganisms is perhaps appropriate in this book, but my present contribution is not intended either as an exhaustive review or as an all-embracing hypothesis. Second, I have given a summary of some evidence obtained by chemists interested in the problems of biosynthesis, dealing with a particular class of secondary metabolites and seeking to define as narrowly as possible the area of biochemical investigation in which a particular problem may be solved; here I have added a speculative exercise that need not be taken too seriously. Finally, I have taken some of the data that accumulate in the not negligible business of *making* natural products and that lead to an investigation of the mechanisms controlling the processes of secondary metabolism in microorganisms.

In each section, then, I have been concerned with the processes by which secondary metabolites are formed, or used, rather than with considerations of any particular microbial products *per se,* as a chemist might be expected to do. In fact, each deals with a field into which the momentum of organic chemistry has carried me, and therefore represents the view of a new arrival attempting to describe strange lands in his own terms. In sparsely inhabited territories, such a new arrival is an explorer who may step out boldly and expect some attention to be paid to his account, but in more populous areas he is an immigrant who must proceed with what propriety he can, and beg for amused tolerance as the least kindness. Where ignorance of local manners—and language—has led me astray, I ask due pardon from the local proprietors.

The honor that an invitation to deliver the Squibb Lectures constitutes is, I feel, a considerable one. In accepting it, I was keenly aware that the magnitude of that honor arises from the distinction of the organizing committee and of the previous contributors to the series. Having made free use of the labors of my own collaborators, more especially of the work of many scientists of far greater merit than mine, I hope that the contribution offered here will not materially have diminished that honor for the future.

J. D. Bu'Lock

Manchester, England.
December 1966

CONTENTS

CHAPTER 3

The Regulation of Secondary Biosynthesis   42

Index   69

Essays in Biosynthesis and Microbial Development

FUNGAL METABOLITES WITH STRUCTURAL FUNCTION

Among the great variety of metabolites which fungi offer for the interest of organic chemists such as myself, it is notorious that there are few satisfactory examples to which any direct biological function can be assigned. In this book, however, I have tried to collect a number of cases in which typical secondary metabolites do seem to have a respectable biological function of a particular kind, namely to act as molecular elements in certain kinds of cell structure. The study of cellular macromolecules is of course a well-established branch of biological investigation, with its own repertoire of techniques and concepts, but from the beginning our own studies have been somewhat differently slanted. Here, I have supplemented the observations of my own colleagues* with parallel instances from a wider field. Most of the examples to be cited come from the higher fungi, Basidiomycetes. This is because the kind of structural function we shall be considering seems to be exercised mainly, or entirely, in specialized parts of the thallus, and particularly in reproductive structures. In the higher fungi such structures are grossly apparent, even to chemists; they

* In this context, notably P. R. Leeming, D. C. Allport, H. G. Smith, B. Kaye, and D. C. Walker.

need no specialized techniques for their separation from the
remainder of the organism and no equipment more elaborate
than a penknife and (sometimes) a ladder. Moreover, the
fruits are often large enough to have provided ample material
for the kind of "natural product investigation" in which
organic chemists like to indulge.

1. Hispidin

Like a certain better-known episode, the story began for us
with the picking of a fruit from a tree. In our case the tree was
an ash tree, *Fraxinus excelsior* L., and the fruit was the shaggy
orange sporophore of *Polyporus hispidus* (Bull.) Fr. In Britain
this occurs fairly commonly on the large isolated ashtrees of
hedgerows, and Cartwright and Findlay (1) describe *P. hispidus*
as the most common cause of heart-rot in the upper trunk of
the ash. The fruits are usually large, often weighing up to a
kilo or more, and our first sample, collected in early August,
afforded quantities of alcohol-soluble phenolic material, from
which we isolated the main component, named it hispidin, and
assigned the structure shown in Figure 1.1(2,3). This was confirmed by the independent work of Edwards et al., who
fortunately used the same name for the pigment (4). From the
comparative point of view this structure is interesting for its
resemblance to a series of pyrone derivatives isolated from
kawa resin (*Piper methysticum*) and from the rosewoods (*Aniba*
spp., etc.) (Figure 1.2), and indeed the trimethyl ether of
hispidin has lately been found in this plant group. However,
the products from higher plants do not include any free
phenols, whereas in *P. hispidus* all the phenolic groups are
unmethylated. The probable biosynthesis of such compounds
is quite clear in outline; those in Figure 1.2 must be formed by
addition of two "acetate units" to nicotinic, benzoic, or
cinnamic acid derivatives, while hispidin itself, the enol-

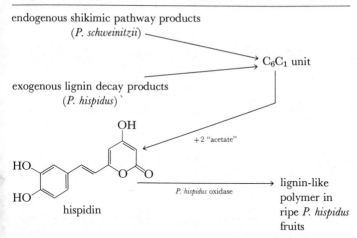

Figure 1.1. The formation and utilization of hispidin in two species of *Polyporus,* the brown-rot *P. schweinitzii,* and the white-rot *P. hispidus.*

lactone of 4-(3,4-dihydroxycinnamoyl)-acetoacetic acid, must arise in a similar manner.

One of the inconveniences of Basidiomycetes is that their fruit-bodies may only appear annually (save for that triumph of applied microbiology, the cultivated mushroom). As a result, our present knowledge of the variation of hispidin content in *P. hispidus* fruits, which gave us a clue as to the function of hispidin, was acquired only after some years of frustration. Eventually we found that sporophores gathered in late July and early August, which are soft and juicy, contain a high proportion of alcohol-soluble pigment, most of which is hispidin. By late August, however, most of the ethanol-soluble pigment appears to be polymeric, with little free hispidin, and by mid-September, when the sporophores have become fibrous and woody, there is little ethanol-soluble material at all. The process of induration during ripening is clearly associated with the disappearance of the soluble phenolics. We also observed

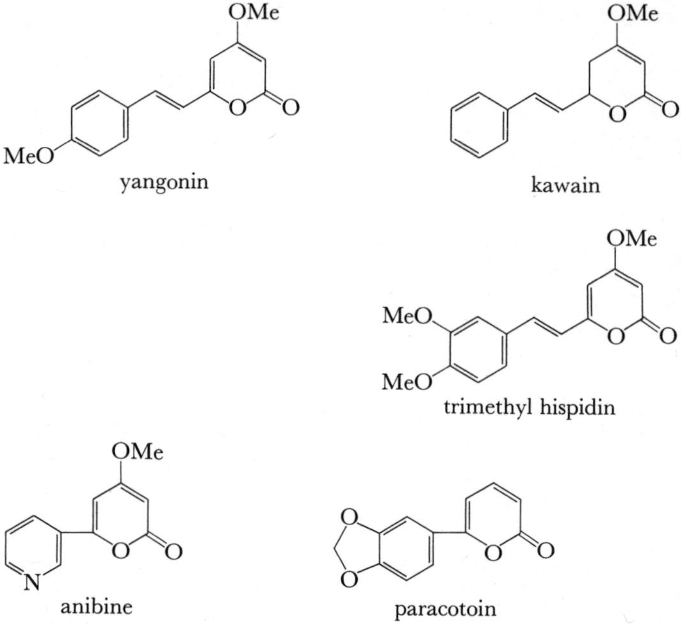

Figure 1.2. Structural relatives of hispidin from higher plants [*Aniba* spp. and *Piper methysticum* ("kawa")].

that the unripe fruits contain a powerful phenol-oxidase system, which effectively oxidizes, for example, catechol, and, more particularly, hispidin. When hispidin is oxidized *in vitro* by the crude enzyme preparation there is no accumulation of quinonoid material, but the light absorption of the hispidin changes in the manner expected for oxidative polymerization. *In vivo* we consider that a similar reaction occurs during ripening, with the important difference that it occurs in a cellular matrix so that the polymer becomes bound to cell materials and effects chemical cross-linking. In this matrix the overall rate of reaction may be limited either by the available oxygen or by a restricted access of enzyme to substrate. Like many other topics of disagreement, the question of the existence of lignins in fungi is largely a matter of definition. In crude analytical terms the polymeric material from *P. hispidus,* with no methoxyl content, does not conform to the lignins of higher plants, but in terms of its function and also of its mode of formation it is completely analogous. Moreover, the monomer, hispidin, is structurally and biogenetically very close to the C_6C_3 precursors of true lignins.

In laboratory cultures, *P. hispidus* grows vegetatively. On normal media the mycelium develops pigmentation quite slowly and no hispidin can be isolated. When it is grown on wood blocks, however, pigmentation is visibly greater and hispidin can be isolated. This phenomenon, typical of many wood-destroying species, seemed worthy of further study. It happened that around this time we were also running a screening program on a Basidiomycete series,* looking for polyacetylenic metabolites, and simultaneously observing a wide range of other products. Among these we found that pigments of hispidin type, as revealed by their ultraviolet spectra, were not infrequent. In particular, we observed such a pigment in quantity in *Polyporus schweinitzii* (Fr.) Pat., and when we grew this on ordinary media we found that hispidin itself was the main product. The isolation from this species has since been reported by Japanese workers (5).

There is an important physiological difference between *P. schweinitzii* and *P. hispidus:* both normally grow on wood, but whereas the former is a well-known example of a "brown-rot," i.e., one which selectively attacks the carbohydrate components of the host timber, *P. hispidus* is an equally typical "white-rot" which attacks both polysaccharide and lignin. Typically, the white-rot species also produce more active

* Very kindly provided by the Forest Products Research Laboratory of Princes Risborough, Berks.

phenol-oxidase enzymes (6). Correlating this with our own observations, the implication is that with the carbohydrates of timber or of ordinary culture media as the main carbon source, *P. schweinitzii* can synthesize all its materials, including the hispidin molecule, and in the absence of phenolases this hispidin can accumulate. By contrast, it is only in the presence of lignin, as well as carbohydrate, that *P. hispidus* can synthesize hispidin in amounts sufficient to leave an isolable surplus over and above the amount being polymerized by its oxidases. When lignin is not supplied, there is little synthesis of hispidin, and all of this is polymerized.

This suggested that the attack on lignin by *P. hispidus* produces hispidin percursors—presumably precursors of the aromatic system. Several studies of lignin breakdown by white-rot fungi have shown that suitable substances can be produced in this way. For example, Ishikawa et al. showed that benzoic and cinnamic acid derivatives and the corresponding aldehydes are produced, and that there is a simultaneous conversion of the original methoxyl groups of the lignin into free phenols (7).

We were able to verify that a variety of compounds of the type which would result from lignin breakdown would indeed replace wood as an accessory requirement for hispidin synthesis by *P. hispidus*. Added at 0.1 to 0.01% concentration to cultures on malt agar, they promoted the accumulation of free hispidin, the identity of which could be verified chromatographically. Positive results were obtained with phenylalanine, tyrosine, *p*-hydroxyphenylpyruvate, *p*-coumaric acid, sinapic acid, syringic acid, etc., and also with shikimic and quinic acids, though not with *p*-hydroxybenzoic, gallic, or caffeic acids, nor with catechol or protocatechuic aldehyde. It is unlikely that all the substances giving positive results are actually being converted into hispidin; some at least may act by sparing effects. The shikimic pathway which is responsible for the normal synthesis of phenylalanine, etc., must be operative in *P. hispidus,* since the organism shows no absolute requirement for these aminoacids, but its capacity is apparently insufficient to allow much diversion of aromatic carbon away from amino-acid synthesis and into hispidin. Since hispidin plays an important role in differentiation of the fruit body in this species, we have here an interesting sidelight on an aspect of parasitism at the molecular level.

2. Naphthalenes and Perylenes

A somewhat different type of structural cross-linking agent was encountered when we examined another fungus which is a common growth upon ash in Britain, the large Ascomycete *Daldinia concentrica.* In 1956 Anderson and Murray described the isolation of 4,9-dihydroxyperylene-3,10-quinone (Figure 1.3) from the hard, coal-black fruits of this species (8). Independently, we had observed rather distinctive ultraviolet absorption spectra in extracts from stock slopes of this fungus and from wild fruits, and from the fruits we were able to isolate (9) a remarkably unstable chromogen which turned out to be the tetrahydroxydinaphthyl shown in Figure 1.3. This substance is very readily oxidized to give a greenish-black polymer, together with small amounts of the perylenequinone as an intramolecular coupling product. The published procedure for the isolation of this quinone from the fruits did not seem very satisfactory to us, since the compound is actually quite insoluble in the solvents used for extraction, so we investigated the matter further. After exhaustive extraction with hexane and ether (which removed *inter alia* triterpenoids, fat, and the tetrahydroxydinaphthyl), extraction with acetone gave a red-brown solution, from which some black material, containing perylenequinone, was deposited. The acetone "solution" showed an absorption spectrum similar to that of

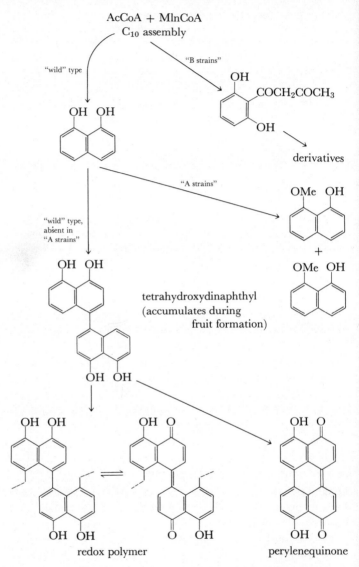

Figure 1.3. Biosynthesis of cross-linking pigment in *Daldinia concentrica*.

8

the insoluble perylenequinone, but the maxima were shifted noticeably. On warming the extract with a little acid more of the quinone was precipitated. It appeared that dispersal of the quinone into the acetone had been assisted by the polar materials (mainly mannitol) also present in the extract, and the possibility of a similar type of molecular association *in vivo* is noteworthy.

The residue after exhaustive extraction of *Daldinia* fruits still retains most of the original pigmentation, and its distinctive microscopic structure is still unchanged. The cell walls contain no true chitin (absence of *N*-acetyl), but are heavily invested with black polymeric pigment, quinonoid in nature, since it is capable of reversible reduction and re-oxidation. Later we showed (10) that the true monomeric chromogen in *D. concentrica* is 1,8-dihydroxynaphthalene. This undergoes oxidative polymerization by coupling at α-positions, generating first the tetrahydroxydinaphthyl, then a polymer, of which the reduced form (Figure 1.3) is simply a 4,5-linked 1,8-dihydroxynaphthalene, but which normally has varying proportions of quinonoid units. A minor intramolecular variant of the coupling gives the perylenequinone. *In vivo,* this oxidative polymerization occurs within the cellular matrix during the differentiation of the fruit-bodies, and thus exerts a cross-linking action. The process is entirely analogous to melanization, e.g., of insect cuticles, and the *Daldinia* black is a type of fungal melanin.

By examination of *D. concentrica* in culture, we also observed an interesting relationship between this functional melanization system and the production of typical secondary metabolites in vegetative cultures (10). From a range of single-spore isolates and from old laboratory stock we selected a number of strains which, in terms of their secondary metabolism, varied between three extreme types (Figure 1.3). The first type, *A*, lacks the oxidase which normally converts 1,8-dihydroxynaph-

xylindein (*Chlorociboria aeruginosa*)

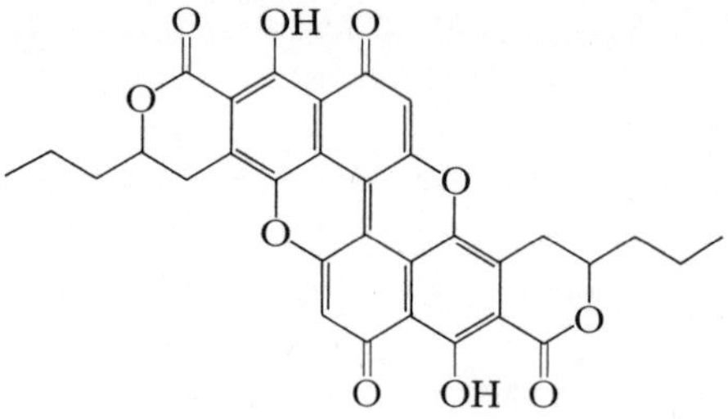

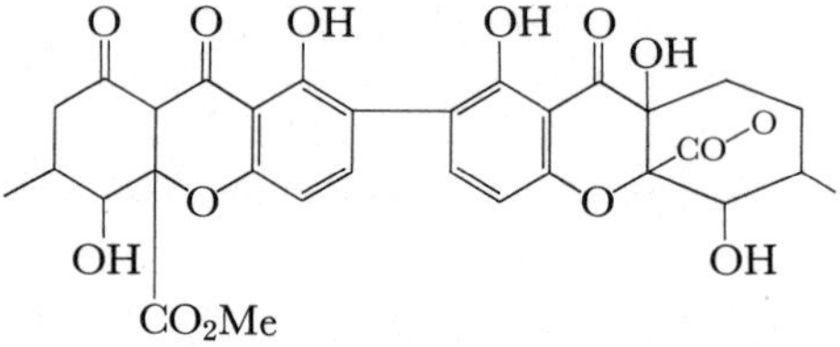

ergochrysin (*Claviceps purpurea*)

Figure 1.4.   Xylindein and the ergot pigments.

thalene into pigment, and instead the chromogen is converted by a side-reaction into its mono- and di-methyl ethers. The second type, *B*, produces a series of derivatives of 2-aceto-acetylresorcinol; this pattern of synthesis results from a defect in the cyclization mechanism normally affording 1,8-dihy-droxynaphthalene, and in the second chapter this type of defect will be considered in more detail. In the third type, *C*, no metabolites relating to this pathway could be detected. It is perhaps worthwhile to remark that had we limited our investigation to stock cultures of *D. concentrica* we should have isolated a series of secondary metabolites of a fairly common kind without any clue as to the importance of the complete pathway in the wild organism.

The synthetic pathways operating in *Daldinia* throw some

light on other fungal products. For example, the "green-stain" fungus *Chlorociboria aeruginosa* produces a polymeric pigment and a dimer, xylindein (Figure 1.4), whose structure has been elucidated and which is quite analogous to the *Daldinia* dinaphthyl. Figure 1.4 also shows one of the pigments of ergot; it shows that in other fungi compounds structurally analogous to the acetoacetylresorcinol derivatives of *Daldinia* can also undergo oxidative dimerization.

3. Fungal Melanins, etc.

The black *Daldinia* pigment is formed when the fruit-bodies develop—one can study this in transverse sections of infected trees, or when conidia form in laboratory cultures; it has a structural role in these differentiated parts of the thallus. It is a fungal melanin, i.e., an irregular quinonoid polymer, linked to cell-materials, formed *in situ* by oxidative polymerization, and capable of reversible reduction and re-oxidation. Pigments thus defined are widespread; notice that their broad definition does not include a specification of the chemical nature of the monomer units. Thus in animals the most common monomer of melanins is 5,6-dihydroxyindole (together with some of its precursors). Professor Nicolaus of Naples has shown how pigments of this kind are accessible to direct chemical investigation by appropriate degradative methods (11), and his more recent studies of nonanimal melanins have revealed an interesting situation. Typical plant melanins afford catechol and related substances on alkali fusion, and the fungal-spore pigment of *Ustilago maydis* is of a similar type (Figure 1.5) (12). On the other hand, the black spore pigment characteristic of many Aspergilli gives mellitic acid on oxidation and apparently has a poly-condensed aromatic structure. Professor Nicolaus informs me that alkali degradation of the *Daldinia* pigment affords a mixture of 1,8-dihydroxynaphthalene (as

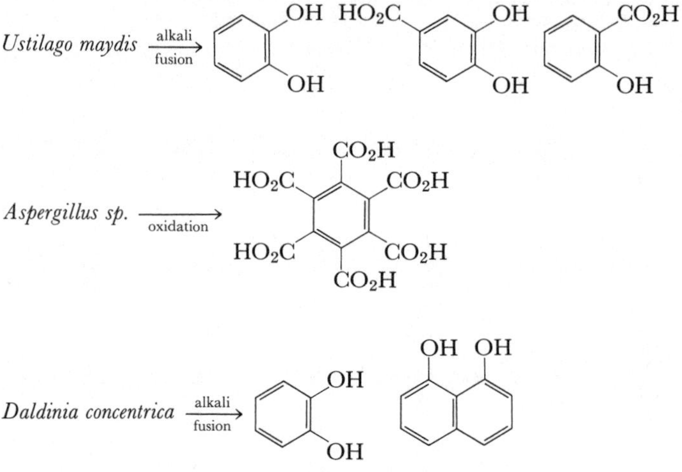
Ustilago maydis
alkali
fusion
OH
OH
HO2C
OH
OH
CO2H
OH
Aspergillus sp.
oxidation
CO2H
HO2C
CO2H
HO2C
CO2H
CO2H
Daldinia concentrica
alkali
fusion
OH
OH
OH OH

Figure 1.5. Degradation products obtained by Nicolaus et al. from fungal melanins.

expected) and catechol; possibly, therefore, the pigment is a copolymer, with catechol oxidation acting as a primer for oxidation of the 1,8-dihydroxynaphthalene.

I have mentioned the somewhat superficial analogy between the *in situ* formation of *Daldinia* melanin etc., and the melanization of insect cuticle. Another analogy is provided by the fungal phenoxazines such as cinnabarin and its derivatives (Figure 1.6). These occur in *Coriolus sanguineus* Fr., where they must be formed by oxidative dimerization of 3-hydroxyanthranilic acid, analogously to the formation of the insect ommochromes, such as xanthommatin, from 3-hydroxykynurenine. Such oxidations can also lead to polymers and copolymers; moreover, in cinnabarins there are functional groups available for cross-linking by ester and amide groups (compare the actinomycin peptides). We suspect that, like hispidin in *P. hispidus,* the isolable cinnabarin merely repre-

cinnabaric acid

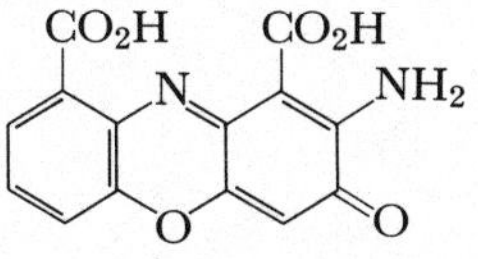

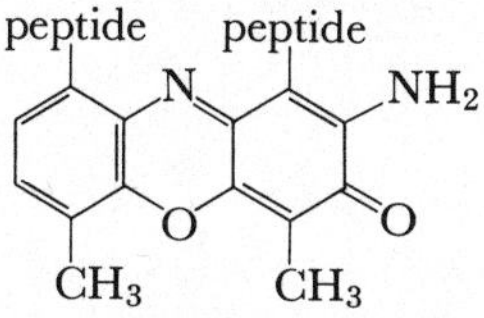

actinomycins

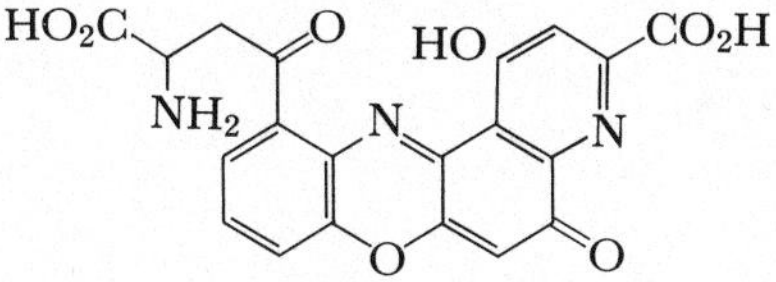

xanthommatin

Figure 1.6.   Cinnabarinic acid, from *Coriolus sanguineus* Fr., and some analogous natural products, the actinomycins and the insect eye pigments.

sents an unused excess of cross-linking agent, and indeed we observed that only a small part of the visible pigment in *C. sanguineus* cultures can be extracted from the thallus.

Another interesting case is offered by the terphenylquinones, such as polyporic acid, and their derivatives (Figure 1.7). Reed and Vining (13) have shown that these are formed by coupling two phenylpropane units, somewhat as in the formation of plant lignins, and recently Mosbach (14) has confirmed the obvious extension that the diphenylbutadiene dicarboxylic acid derivatives, such as pulvic "anhydride," which have a very similar distribution, are formed from the terphenyl-quinones by fission of the central ring. These compounds occur

polyporic acid (*Polyporus* spp., etc.)

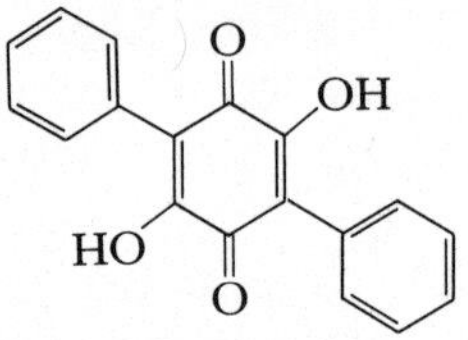

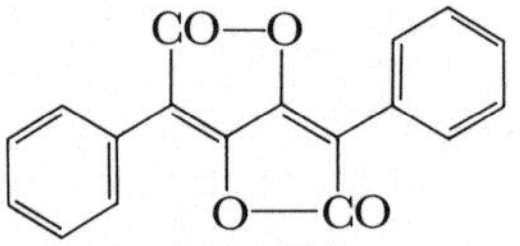

pulvic anhydride (*Sticta* spp., etc.)

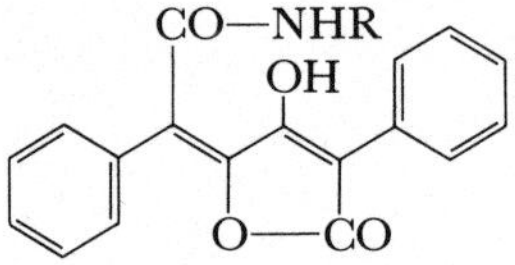

R = PhCH$_2$CH·CO$_2$H   rhizocarpic acid

R = Me$_2$CH·CH$_2$CH·CO$_2$Me   epanorin

Figure 1.7.   Terphenyl derivatives from fungi and lichens.

widely, often in large amounts, in the fruits of Basidiomycetes and also in lichens (where they are produced by the fungal component). The parent quinones are potential cross-linking agents and so also are their fission products, for the enol-lactone groups of pulvic "anhydride" indeed show anhydride-like reactivity, and could act as cross-linking agents for either proteins or polysaccharides. In fact, at least two amides formed from pulvic anhydride and common aminoacids have been isolated from lichens (Figure 1.7), and serve to illustrate this possibility.

4. Chagi

In *Polyporus hispidus* we described a fungal lignin based upon a monomer which itself was elaborated using lignin breakdown products from the host tree as part precursor. Now, the substance "chagi," as described by Shivrina and her coworkers in Leningrad (15), is in many ways comparable. Chagi is a material obtained by hot-water extraction of the abortive fructifications of a white-rot fungus *Poria obliqua* ($\equiv$*Inonotus obliquus* Pers.) Bres., found upon birch trees in Siberia and also, happily for us, in Scotland. Medicinal properties have been claimed for the infusion, which contains a very high concentration of colloidally dispersed phenolics. The Russian workers obtained a small yield of aromatic aldehydes by prolonged acid treatment of chagi; the mixture is similar to that obtained from lignin, and they postulated that the chagi derived from the lignin of the host tree.

The chagi which we have examined seems to be in every way intermediate in properties between "typical lignins" and the even more vaguely defined humic acids. Compared to lignins, chagi contains less methoxyl and more phenolic and acidic groups. Degradation by the methods of lignin chemistry confirmed the Russian observations, yielding in every case mixtures of *p*-hydroxyphenyl, vanillyl, and sinapyl derivatives, mostly of C_6C_1 type, but with some C_6C_3 units. The polymer contains no simple ester groups and no large number of quinonoid or catechol groups, though it gives a semiquinone electron-spin resonance signal, and catechols are generated in large amount in the polymer by reductive fission with sodium amalgam. Analyses of various methylated and hydrolyzed products, and direct potentiometric titrations, give consistent values for the content of phenolic and carboxylic acid groups. Without any implications as to the size of the monomer units (which are probably a mixture of C_6C_1 and C_6C_3) we can write empirical formulae such as

$$C_{7.0}H_{5.3}O_{1.7}(OMe)_{0.35}(OH)_{0.7}(O_2H)_{0.5}$$

where (OH) and (O_2H) are phenolic and carboxylic units respectively. From our infra-red data it appears that part of the remaining oxygen present is as aliphatic H-bonded hydroxyl, and the rest is probably combined in aryl ether links; the resistance of the polymer to breakdown suggests that it is linked by C—C and ether bonds.

Spectroscopic examination by the lignin methods developed by Aulin-Erdtman (16) could also be applied to chagi. In this way we found that about half the phenolic groups are in units of the simple hydroxybenzene type, and a further 40% are in *p*-hydroxybenzoic acid type units; the remaining minority are in *p*-hydroxybenzoyl and *p*-hydroxycinnamoyl chromophores. These data are consistent with the chemical analyses, and they imply a preponderance of C_6C_1 units. It seems that *P. obliqua* is able to polymerize fairly directly the type of lignin breakdown products (7) which in *P. hispidus* are first converted into hispidin. In both fungi the polymerization is confined to the sporophore (which is not, of course, the site where the lignin is being attacked), and occurs there as part of the process of sporophore differentiation; in both species the extractable pigment only represents the less firmly bound portion of this structural material.

5. Miscellanea

For many other fungal metabolites, functions of the kind I have described must be considered plausible. The frequent isolation from the same or related sources of monomeric products and the corresponding dimers (as in the fungal anthraquinones or in the lichen depsides) seems itself to imply the existence of similar polymers—which of course would be far less tractable for laboratory study. Many of the simple aromatic metabolites obtainable from fungi in culture could easily generate polymers of the catechol-melanin type, and all such polymerizations, *in situ,* will imply a cross-linking of cell or cell-wall components. Cross-linking by other means, such as ester or amide linkages, is also very likely. One is reminded of the luteic acid, a poly-malonylglucose, produced by certain imperfect fungi (17, 18), and in this connection we have observed that a surprisingly high proportion of ^{14}C-malonate taken up by *Penicillium urticae* becomes bound to insoluble cell material. There may be parallels to the function of dipicolinic acid in spores.

[Since these lectures were delivered, Dr. N. McCorkindale of the University of Glasgow has informed me of their work on *Polyporus betulinus,* a characteristically "woody" but nonpigmented Basidiomycete fruit containing a high proportion of triterpenoids. In young fruits a large part of the triterpene content is present in combination with dibasic acids such as malonic and mevalonic. Such linkages seem to offer us a further possible type of cross-linking agent.]

In laboratory cultures the production of secondary metabolites of the kind we have considered here is usually favored by nutritional and other conditions which are parallel to, if not always quite identical with, those favoring the formation of various kinds of fruiting structures. Often such compounds are visibly located within such structures. The connections between secondary metabolism and morphological development are too complex for us to explore here, and indeed the subject is one for future study rather than for present review. One aspect is touched upon in the third chapter; here I have simply tried to show the existence of one further facet: how in certain circumstances typical secondary metabolites can be found "in use," and how even for organic chemists the study of a natural product is not simply a matter of isolation, characterization, and synthesis.

REFERENCES

1. Cartwright, K. St. G., and W. P. K. Findlay, *Decay of Timber and Its Prevention* (second ed.), H. M. Stationery Office, London, 1958, p. 137.
2. Bu'Lock, J. D., P. R. Leeming, and H. G. Smith, *Experientia,* **17,** 553 (1961).
3. Bu'Lock, J. D., and H. G. Smith, *J. Chem. Soc.,* 2085 (1962).
4. Edwards, R. L., D. G. Lewis, and D. V. Wilson, *J. Chem. Soc.,* 4995 (1961).
5. Ueno, A., S. Fukushima, Y. Saiki, and T. Harada, *Chem. Pharm. Bull. (Japan),* **12,** 376 (1964).
6. Davidson, R. W., D. J. Campbell, and D. J. Blaisdell, *J. Agri. Res.,* **57,** 683 (1938).
7. Ishikawa, H., W. J. Schubert, and F. F. Nord, *Arch. Biochem. Biophys.,* **100,** 131 and 140 (1963).
8. Anderson, A., and J. Murray, *Chem. Ind. (London),* 376 (1956).
9. Bu'Lock, J. D., and D. C. Allport, *J. Chem. Soc.,* 4090 (1958).
10. Allport, D. C., and J. D. Bu'Lock, *J. Chem. Soc.,* 654 (1960).
11. Piatelli, M., E. Fattorusso, S. Magno, and R. A. Nicolaus, *Tetrahedron,* **19,** 2061 (1963).
12. Piatelli, M., G. Fattorusso, S. Magno, and R. A. Nicolaus, *Tetrahedron Letters,* **15,** 997 (1963).
13. Reed, G., L. C. Vining, and R. H. Haskins, *Can. J. Chem.,* **40,** 2357 (1962).
14. Mosbach, K., *Biochem. Biophys. Res. Commun.,* **17,** 363 (1964).
15. Loviagina, E. V., A. N. Shivrina, and E. G. Platonova, *Biokhimiya,* **25,** 640 (1960) and earlier papers.
16. Aulin-Erdtman, G., *Svensk Papperstid.,* **56,** 287 (1953); *cf. Svensk Kem. Tidskr.,* **70,** 4 (1958).
17. Anderson, C. G., W. N. Haworth, H. Raistrick, and M. Stacey, *Biochem. J.,* **33,** 272 (1939).
18. Baddiley, P. J., *J. Chem. Soc.,* 1944 (1953).

2

MECHANISMS OF POLYKETIDE
SYNTHESIS

1. The Nature of Polyketides

In the previous Chapter I illustrated ways in which an organic chemist's investigations of natural products can lead to considerations of morphological function. In the present one, I shall attempt to set out a chemist's approach to certain questions of biochemical mechanism which might be thought to belong more properly to the enzymologist. The pioneer studies of Birch and coworkers (1) defined a whole class of natural products, the *polyketides,* in terms of a biosynthetic mechanism, *viz* the assembly and chemically rational transformation of alternately-oxygenated chains formed from two-carbon units metabolically related to acetic acid. Chemists concerned with the elucidation of structures arising by such processes are naturally led to enquire into the mechanisms by which they are formed, and here I shall attempt to describe some conclusions arising from these enquiries.

First let us consider the general nature of the polyketides—briefly, since they are the subject of several reviews (2, 3, 4)—and try to assess their biochemical importance. We must begin with the ubiquitous fatty acids, since in the broadest sense of the term, these are polyketides, and the well-known facts concerning their synthesis are, as we shall see, very relevant to our problem. However, it will be better for us to use the term polyketides in a more restricted sense, because in several important ways the fatty acids stand somewhat apart. In this more restricted sense, the most typical polyketides are aromatic compounds, of varying complexity ranging from, say, orsellinic acid (Figure 2.1) to the tetracyclines (Figure 2.2), with multiple oxygen functions showing a marked tendency to occur on alternate carbon atoms. Orsellinic acid is a "simple" polyketide, but most of the natural products have additional structural features, some of which can be shown to arise by reactions subsequent to polyketide synthesis proper. Others

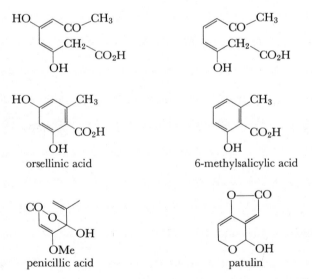

orsellinic acid

6-methylsalicylic acid

penicillic acid

patulin

Figure 2.1.   Orsellinic and 6-methylsalicylic acids, two simple polyketides, with their hypothetical polyketoacid precursors above, and two of their further metabolites below.

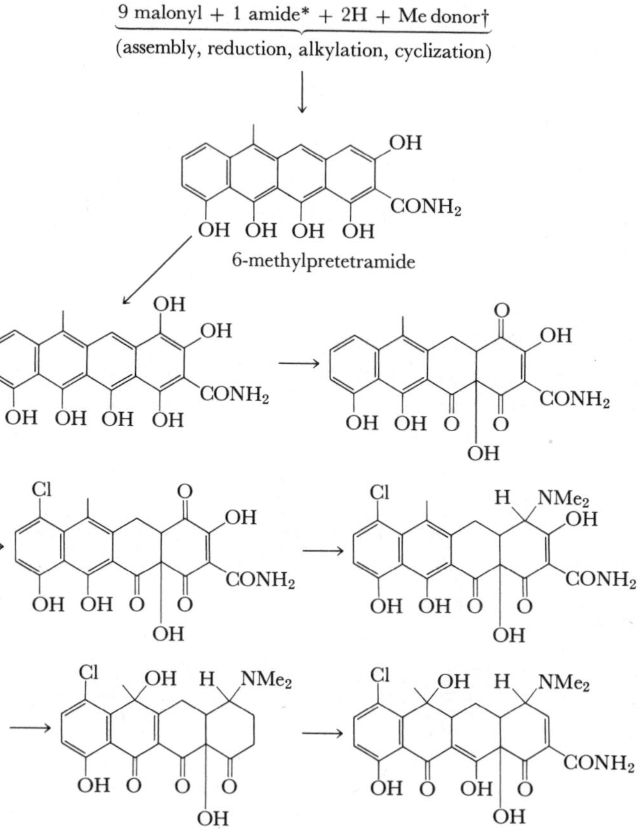

9 malonyl + 1 amide* + 2H + Me donor†

(assembly, reduction, alkylation, cyclization)

6-methylpretetramide

Figure 2.2.   Stages in chlorotetracycline formation. In the first reaction-step, the malonamide starter* may be replaced by acetoacetate, and the methyl donor† is not essential. Subsequent reactions involve one or more steps.

arise by processes which are additional to this key step but which nevertheless appear to be closely integrated with it. For example, Figure 2.1 shows the derivation of penicillic acid from orsellinic acid, as demonstrated by Mosbach (5), and

Figure 2.2 shows McCormick's interpretation (6) of the formation of tetracyclines from the parent pretetramides. These sequences typify the transformations which may follow after polyketide synthesis. However, in the pretetramides themselves, the absence of oxygen at $C_{(8)}$ and the (optional) methyl group at $C_{(6)}$, are features which seem to be introduced during the actual synthesis of the polyketide system.

If the fatty acids are excluded, the aromatic polyketides (and some related nonaromatic products) are seen as secondary metabolites *par excellence,* for none is known to play any well-defined direct role in primary metabolism. Their natural distribution is also typical of secondary metabolites: individual products are obtained from particular species or small groups of species, and even the "parent polyketides" such as orsellinic acid have very restricted taxonomic ranges. On the other hand, the general process of polyketide synthesis is not trivially distributed; it is very common in fungi, frequent in actinomycetes and in higher plants, occasional in bacteria and invertebrates, and probably absent in higher animals. Special kinds of polyketide are fairly characteristic of some of these large taxonomic groups. Thus a variant in which the chains are built up from methylmalonyl ("propionate") units, and are rather extensively reduced, as in the macrolides, is characteristic of actinomycetes (in which a similar variant of fatty-acid synthesis is also found). Again, the use of shikimic-derived aromatic acids as starter units, as in the flavonoids, is a feature of polyketides in higher plants. Such special cases have their particular implications; in the broader view, when the problems of polyketide synthesis are considered in general terms, they obviously concern an activity which is sufficiently widespread to constitute a biochemical problem of respectable proportions. I emphasize this point of biochemical respectability since many biochemists have been reluctant to consider the problems of secondary metabolism at all. To them, perhaps, the very existence of secondary metabolites threatens not only the dogma of biochemical unity but also the superstition of biochemical teleology. Consequently, our knowledge of the "natural products" comes mainly from the work of organic chemists, and it has only recently reached the stage where the problems of secondary metabolism can be posed in biochemical terms. There is also the experimental fact—ruefully admitted by many distinguished workers—that many of the most important enzyme systems which carry out secondary biosynthetic processes have, for some inscrutable reason, proved very elusive when pursued by the classical biochemical method of enzymological study in cell-free systems. Thus most of the evidence we can collect on the mechanism of polyketide synthesis will come from *ad hoc* "chemists' experiments," using intact cells and operating in a conceptual framework which the average biochemist finds unfamiliar and even unconvincing.

2. Polyketides and Fatty Acids

From the elementary observation that polyketides and the common fatty acids share the same biogenetic constitution, *viz,* the chain of "acetate-derived" subunits, we can usefully continue by comparing the details of fatty-acid synthesis as now understood with the corresponding features of polyketide synthesis so far as they are known (7).

Fatty-acid synthesis requires a "starter," usually, but not inevitably, acetyl-CoA, and a series of chain units, normally, but not invariably, provided by malonyl-CoA, itself formed from acetyl-CoA by carboxylation. These coenzyme-A derivatives are separately converted into corresponding thioesters of the acyl-carrier-protein (CP). Acetyl-CP and malonyl-CP then combine to form acetoacetyl-CP; this is reduced (stepwise) to butyryl-CP which in turn reacts with a further molecule of malonyl-CP, and so on. The chain-length of the final product is probably determined less by the specificity of the synthesizing enzymes than by the specificity of deacylases or transacylases which finally remove the products from the acyl carrier system. While still attached to the carrier protein, the products may undergo further reactions, such as dehydrogenation of the chain at specific points to afford the common unsaturated acids like oleic acid. The general character of the system is represented in Figure 2.3.

Because of the participation of the special carrier protein, intermediates between the acetyl- and malonyl-CoA derivatives and the final products are not normally in equilibrium with any other cell components; this is, effectively, an "all-or-nothing" system that is not accessible to intermediates which are not bound to the carrier protein. For instance, the acetoacetyl-CoA which is an intermediate in isoprenoid synthesis does not normally equilibrate with the acetoacetyl-CP which is

$$CH_3CO \cdot S \cdot CoA + HS \cdot CP \rightleftharpoons CH_3CO \cdot S \cdot CP + CoA \cdot SH$$
$$CH_2(CO_2^-)CO \cdot S \cdot CoA + HS \cdot CP \rightleftharpoons$$
$$CH_2(CO_2^-)CO \cdot S \cdot CP + CoA \cdot SH$$
$$*CH_3CO \cdot S \cdot CP + CH_2(CO_2^-)CO \cdot S \cdot CP \longrightarrow$$
$$CH_3CO \cdot CH_2CO \cdot S \cdot CP + CO_2 + HS \cdot CP$$
$$CH_3CO \cdot CH_2CO \cdot S \cdot CP \xrightarrow[\text{(steps)}]{} CH_3CH_2CH_2CO \cdot S \cdot CP$$

$$CH_3CH_2CH_2CO \cdot S \cdot CP + CH_2(CO_2^-)CO \cdot S \cdot CP \longrightarrow \text{(etc.)}$$

$$\xrightarrow[\text{(e.g.)}]{} CH_3(CH_2)_{16}CO \cdot S \cdot CP \longrightarrow \text{stearic derivatives}$$

$$\downarrow O_2, \text{enzyme}$$

$$CH_3(CH_2)_7 \cdot CH{=}CH \cdot (CH_2)_7 \cdot CO \cdot S \cdot CP \longrightarrow \text{oleic derivatives}$$

Figure 2.3.   Fatty-acid synthesis. CP · SH is the protein equivalent of CoA · SH; note how all intermediates beyond acetyl- and malonyl-CoA are bound to this special protein, and how other reactions may intervene before the assembled acid is split off from the carrier protein. The assembly step is marked.*

an intermediate in fatty-acid synthesis, even when both synthetic routes are operating simultaneously.

To what extent are these features found in the synthesis of aromatic polyketides? The role of acetic-acid derivatives was established experimentally by Birch et al. (8) in 1955, and the participation of coenzyme-A derivatives by Tanenbaum and Bassett in 1960 in one of the few successful experiments using cell-free preparations (9). The involvement of malonyl derivatives, analogously to their role in fatty-acid synthesis, was demonstrated independently by Bentley and Keil in Pittsburgh (10) and by my own group in Manchester (11). Direct evidence for a specific carrier is not available, but it is well known that polyketide synthesis shows "all-or-nothing" characteristics. The last intermediates susceptible to endogenous or exogenous dilution are acetyl- and malonyl-CoA (12), and it is quite easy to obtain differential isotope incorporation into polyketides and fatty acids on the one hand, and into the isoprenoids on the other (12). In suitable cases polyketides can be labeled distinguishably from acetoacetyl residues (13). The requirement for acetyl as the starter unit is not absolutely inflexible, and in orsellinic-acid synthesis, added propionate can be incorporated in its place (14). There are many examples of special systems which use other starter units in a specific manner, and actinomycetes, which will utilize methylmalonyl-CoA for the synthesis of branched-chain fatty acids, are also well known as producers of the characteristic "propionate-derived" macrolides like erythromycin (15).

3. The Special Features of Polyketide Synthesis

Certainly, then, the analogy between fatty-acid synthesis and polyketide synthesis is more than superficial, and it will be more profitable now to examine their differences. The key distinction is that polyketide synthesis is essentially nonreductive (Figure 2.4). Thus, for example, orsellinic acid is at the same oxidation level as the hypothetic β-polyketoacid $CH_3CO(CH_2CO)_3OH$, and on paper it can be derived from such an acid simply by aldol condensation, eliminating one oxygen as H_2O and enolizing two others. Isotope experiments indeed confirm that the oxygen atoms of orsellinic acid are derived from the acetyl-CoA precursor (16). More complex polyketides are similarly related to higher β-polyketoacids; in some, a certain number of reductive steps must be included in the synthesis. Thus 6-methylsalicylic acid is built up from four C_2 units (acetyl + 3 malonyl) analogously to orsellinic acid,

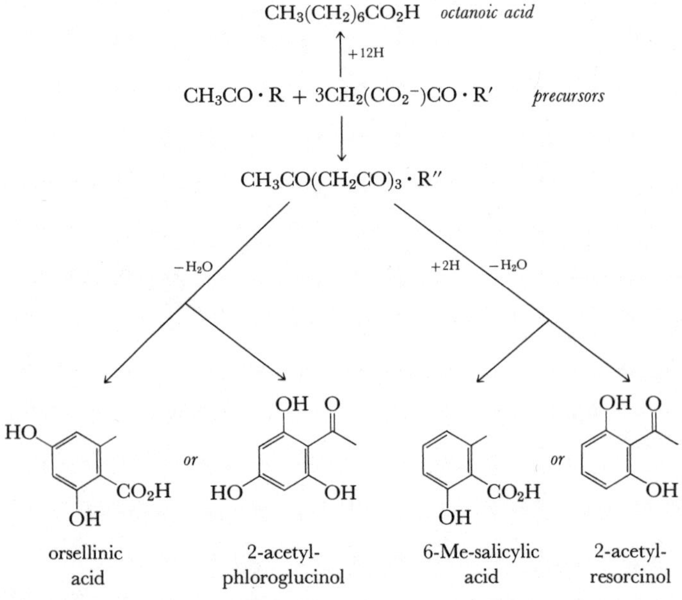

Figure 2.4. Stoichiometry of the reductive process of fatty-acid synthesis, of nonreductive polyketide synthesis, and of polyketide synthesis with minor reductive step(s), also showing alternative cyclizations of the C_8 chain.

but at some stage the equivalent of two hydrogen atoms is taken up. The hypothetical ketoacid corresponding to 6-methylsalicylic acid would be

$$CH_3CO \cdot CH{=}CH \cdot CH_2CO \cdot CH_2CO_2H;$$

in this instance Lynen has confirmed that reduction is an integral part of the synthesis, and the hydride donor is identified as TPNH (17). A similar reductive step is presumed to be responsible for the absence of oxygen at $C_{(8)}$ of the pretetramides and of the derived tetracyclines (Figure 2.2).

4. Polyketoacyls

In fatty-acid synthesis the reduction steps which convert β-ketoacyl-CP are necessarily interposed among successive chain-extensions (Figure 2.3). In some circumstances, and in the absence of hydride donors, further condensation of the acetoacetyl-CP has been observed (18), giving a $\beta\delta$-diketohexanoyl derivative in low yield. The process stops at this stage and the product is readily hydrolyzed, and no higher β-polyketoacyls are produced. By itself, therefore, the type of assembly system which operates in fatty-acid synthesis is not capable of producing the β-polyketoacyl systems from which aromatic polyketides might be formed. Moreover, though the reactions by which a β-polyketoacyl might be converted into an aromatic polyketide are chemically feasible, the spontaneous reactions of such compounds, when prepared in the laboratory, are usually of a different kind, with a marked tendency to the formation of pyrones and similar oxygen heterocycles. *In vivo*, too, the mere formation of the requisite type of polyketoacyl is not sufficient. For example, in the fungus *Daldinia concentrica* which I mentioned in the first chapter, the normal intermediate 1,8-dihydroxynaphthalene is a polyketide to which the variant product 2-acetoacetylresorcinol corresponds as a partly

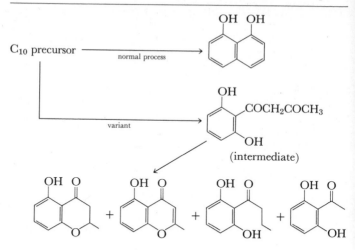

Figure 2.5.   Effect of defective cyclization in *Daldinia concentrica;* the aceto-acetylresorcinol is not an intermediate in the normal pathway and is converted into the four nonnaphthalenic products shown.

cyclized polyketoacyl. The complete cyclization of this variant product would, in chemical terms, appear feasible, but in practice it does not occur. Instead, the incompletely cyclized product is released (as the pyrone), or is partly hydrolyzed to the acetophenone, as shown in Figure 2.5 (19). Similarly, in the tetracycline series, partly cyclized products can be obtained from certain mutant organisms, and these are not then susceptible to complete cyclization, either spontaneously or *in vivo* (Figure 2.6).

In any case, we must provide for a mechanism of cyclization which can be *specific,* in the sense of imposing particular arrangements upon the β-polyketoacyl chain. To take a very simple example, the same C_8 chain that is seen in orsellinic acid is also used, in a quite different range of organisms, for the synthesis of acetylphloroglucinol derivatives (Figure 2.4).

Moreover, when we consider some of the more complex poly-ketide systems, such as the pretetramides, we see that, counting from the "starter" unit, the minimum length of β-polyketoacyl chain that must be attained before *any* of the requisite cycliza-tion steps can take place is already more than sufficient to form, say, orsellinic acid, so that there must be specific factors preventing the simpler modes of cyclization.

One kind of mechanism which has sometimes been con-sidered should be examined at this point. This supposes an enzyme matrix of the requisite geometry, with binding-sites (thiol groups) for all the component acetyl and malonyl sub-units, at which the subunits can be attached individually and

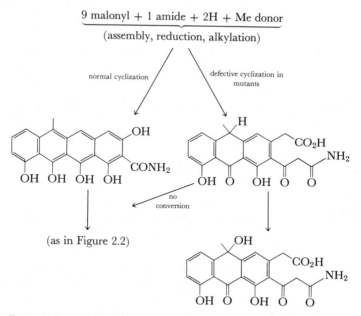

Figure 2.6. Evidence for separation of the cyclization step in pretetramide synthesis from the assembly process and related reactions.

reversibly. The matrix is supposed to be so arranged that when all the binding-sites are occupied, the subunits will combine in a concerted manner, giving the aromatic polyketide directly. Such a mechanism would have the required "all-or-nothing" characteristic and the desired specificity, and would avoid the complications of postulating actual polyketoacyls as intermediates. However, even a simple polyketide such as orsellinic acid would require a matrix with at least four binding-sites, and for more complex products ten or more such sites might be required, in addition to the structural features necessary to orient the subunits and promote their reaction. These requirements seem to me prohibitively complex; moreover, such a mechanism for polyketide synthesis would be quite unrelated to the fatty-acid mechanism—or indeed to any known enzymic process. In any case, there are some further features of secondary polyketide synthesis which seem to imply the existence of actual intermediates which are fully assembled but which have not yet assumed the final cyclized aromatic arrangement.

We have already noted the pair of compounds, acetyl-phloroglucinol and orsellinic acid, in which the same polyketide assembly has been cyclized in different patterns. Such examples can be multiplied, and in addition (Figure 2.7), we can find examples of the converse relationship, i.e., compounds in which the same cyclization pattern has been imposed upon quite different polyketide chains. These cases suggest, though they do not require, that polyketide assembly and polyketide cyclization are distinguishable processes. Some confirmation for this view comes from studies of genetically determined variations in polyketide synthesis, since we have examples of pathways in which the cyclization process is partly defective, while the assembly process is unchanged. Complete assembly, with defective cyclization, is seen in the resorcinols from *Daldinia concentrica* (Figure 2.5), and in the anthracenes pro-

endocrocin

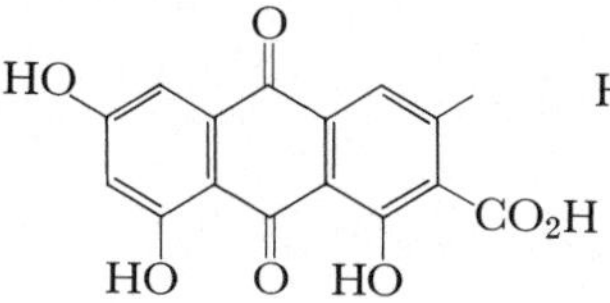

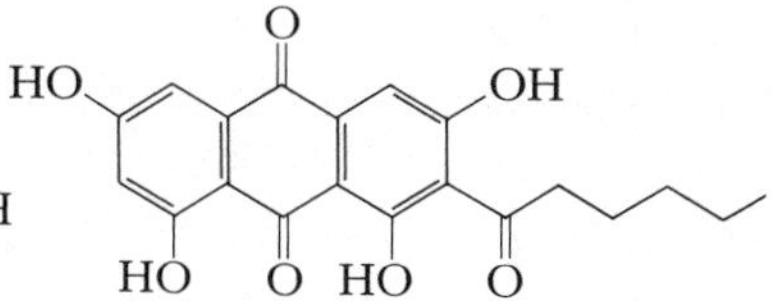

solorinic acid

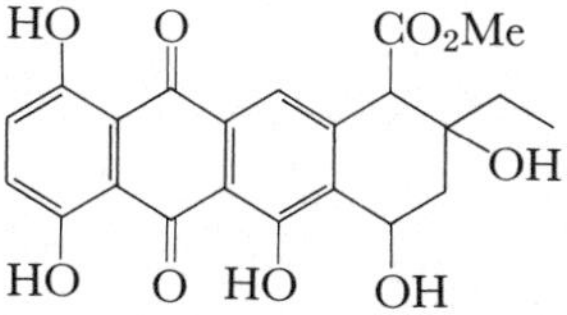

rutilantinone

Figure 2.7. In these anthraquinones, the same specific cyclization pattern has been imposed upon polyketoacyls of different chain length, which are differently oriented in the cyclization matrix.

duced by certain mutants in the tetracycline series (Figure 2.6).

Some insight into the nature of the assembly prior to cyclization can be obtained from a consideration of those additional reactions which, as mentioned at the beginning of the chapter, seem to be inseparable from the overall step of polyketide synthesis. As examples (Figure 2.2), we considered the optional methyl group at $C_{(6)}$ of the tetracyclines and the absence of oxygen at $C_{(8)}$; these are features which are already present in the first free intermediates, the pretetramides, in contrast to all the other structural features of tetracyclines which are demonstrably introduced by subsequent transformations (6). Thus, if to a mutant defective in the stage of pretetramide synthesis, and derived from a C-methylating parent, we supply the nonmethylated pretetramide, only nonmethylated tetracyclines are produced.

There are no such precise observations for the deoxygenation step, either in the tetracycline series (where the 8-hydroxy series is unknown), or in such pairs as orsellinic and 6-methyl-salicylic acids, but there is a general consensus of evidence that these reduction reactions can be similarly integrated with polyketide synthesis. This applies equally to some other C-alkylations, e.g., by isopentenyl and polyisoprenoid residues. We shall see shortly that the positions in the β-polyketoacyl chain at which reductive deoxygenation can occur are significant. The positions at which C-alkylation can occur are also informative. A variety of experiments show that the alkylating agents are the conventional ones, i.e., S-adenosylmethionine for C-methylations and isoprenoid pyrophosphates for the isopentenylations, etc. Alkylation invariably occurs on the alternate, nonoxygenated, atoms of the chain, and we therefore conclude that in the assembly these positions must remain susceptible to electrophilic substitution, since in the final poly-ketide the corresponding positions will not always have the appropriate reactivity.

We therefore require, for the "polyketoacyl" intermediates, a type of structure which

(a) can be assembled by a process at least similar to that in fatty-acid synthesis, without exceeding reasonable limits of chemical instability;

(b) can accommodate from four to at least ten C_2 units;

(c) is stabilized and conformationally controlled by an acceptable type of multi-point attachment, in a manner subject to modification as a result of genetic mutations;

(d) has at least some of the alternate carbon atoms susceptible to electrophilic attack and certain oxygen atoms susceptible to hydride reduction;

(e) is ultimately capable of specific cyclization reactions.

5. Stabilization by Chelation

One well-known property of enolizable β-diketones and similar compounds is their ability to form coordination com-

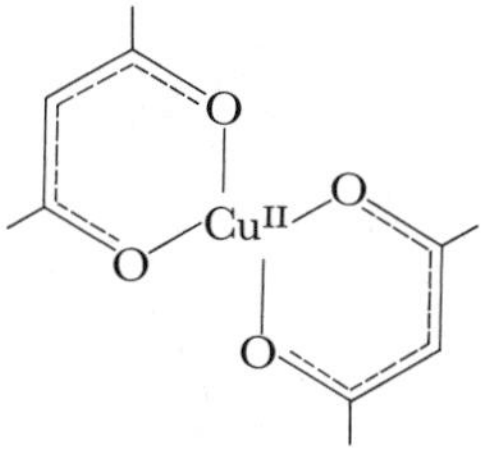

Figure 2.8.   Cupric acetylacetone chelate.

plexes with metal ions. For example, the half-enol of acetyl-acetone forms the copper derivative shown in Figure 2.8, which has quasi-aromatic character. In such complexes, electrophilic substitution is facilitated; complexing is favored by the electronic delocalization, but it is easily reversible. The coordination geometry of the metal atom determines the overall conformation of the complex. Now, if we go on to consider possible ways of forming similar complexes from, say, the C_8 triketoacyl chain which is the simplest of the polyketide precursors (cf. Figure 2.4), we find that of the four available oxygen atoms, there are three which can conveniently be used to coordinate with a metal ion having an appropriate arrangement of ligands. Moreover, this threefold coordination can be set up in two ways, as schematized in Figure 2.9. If we denote the thioester carbonyl of the C_8 chain as a, and the other carbonyls in order b, c, d, then one arrangement involves coordination with a, b, and d (Figure 2.9a), and the other with a, c, and d (Figure 2.9b). Each of these arrangements has the same geometry around the metal ion, and in each the triketoacyl chain is favorably conformed, in two virtually planar portions separated by the one unemployed carbonyl group (which need not be enolized). Now it is very striking that these two possible foldings of the triketoacyl ligand should correspond so precisely to the foldings of the chain in the two basic types of C_8 polyketide, orsellinic acid and acetylphloroglucinol respectively.

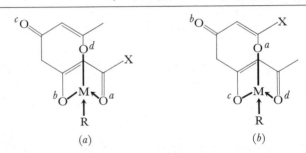

Figure 2.9.   Alternative patterns of chelation of a triketoacyl derivative
$CH_3CO(CH_2CO)_3X$ with a metal ion, where R represents one or more additional ligands.

Moreover, the unemployed carbonyl groups in each case are precisely those which are absent in the corresponding deoxygenated series based on 6-methylsalicyclic acid and 2-acetyl resorcinol respectively (Figure 2.4). It thus appears that chelation in a complex of this kind fulfills, in a remarkably simple way, several of the requirements arrived at in our earlier examination. Our next step must be to enquire

(a) whether such an assembly can feasibly be transformed into the corresponding type of aromatic system, and

(b) whether such an assembly can be put together by a reasonable variation of the condensation step in fatty-acid synthesis.

There is a further question, namely, whether similar mechanisms can be applied to the synthesis of more complex polyketides. I have no doubt that they can, but the demonstration of their feasibility involves an unduly prolonged exercise in speculation. I am satisfied that there is nothing that we now know about the synthesis of these more complex products that cannot be accommodated within the present hypothesis, but our next steps involve more detailed arguments which would appear wildly speculative in anything but the simplest cases, to which the discussion is therefore confined.

6. Aromatization

A few years ago, several chemists (myself included) considered that the naturally occurring polyacetylenes, which are clearly fatty-acid variants, might be derived from ketoacyl precursors by an elimination reaction of the enolic forms. This would require that the enolic oxygen should be combined in a suitable leaving-group. There resulted from such speculations two new laboratory syntheses of triple bonds (20, 21), one of which clearly demonstrated that a reaction of the type

$$-\overset{\overset{\displaystyle H}{|}}{C}=\overset{\underset{\displaystyle OX}{|}}{C}- \quad\longrightarrow\quad -C\equiv C-$$

can occur readily in certain circumstances. Today, it seems rather unlikely that this particular reaction actually occurs biologically, but its discovery makes at least plausible a hypothetical variation shown in Figure 2.10, in which the vinylic $=$CH— and the enolic $\overset{|}{=}$C—OX are suitably situated but not directly connected, so that the elimination reaction now leads to a ring-closure. Now, the stereoelectronic requirements for such a reaction are in fact met by the metal-triketoacyl complexes of Figure 2.9, so that these *stabilizing* complexes may also offer us a built-in mechanism for the *aromatization* step. There is the question whether the metal-oxygen group which would be involved (*cf.* Figure 2.9) can ever constitute a suitable leaving-group: since the metal cannot be identified by *a priori* arguments this question can scarcely be considered, but the range of properties available

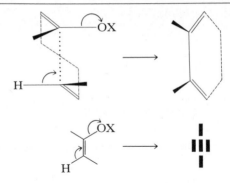

Figure 2.10. Stereoelectronic requirements for a hypothetical cyclization reaction (above) and the analogous laboratory reaction leading to a triple bond (below).

in metal ions, probably modified by other ligands, is so wide that the possibility can hardly be excluded.

7. Assembly

We are enquiring whether a suitable polyketoacyl-assembly mechanism can be devised which is comparable to the condensation reaction in normal fatty-acid synthesis: accordingly, we must first examine this condensation reaction. The overall reaction is between an enzyme and the acetyl- (or higher acyl-) and malonyl-derivatives of the carrier protein (CP). For this, a stepwise mechanism is most likely; first, either an acetyl-enzyme or a malonyl-enzyme will be formed, and this will react with malonyl-CP or acetyl-CP, as appropriate, in the second step. Irrespective of details, part of the driving force of the condensation reaction will be the decarboxylation, and part must be the release of the thiol originally combined in the "anhydride-like" acetyl- or acyl-derivative. Thus it will be the thioester group of the malonyl-derivative which remains intact in the acetoacetyl product. Nevertheless, in subsequent reactions this furnishes the higher acyl group for the next condensation cycle, which will now occupy a "malonyl site" (either on the enzyme or on the carrier protein; see above). It is unlikely that the enzyme and the carrier protein are so equivalent that it is matter of indifference which reaction moiety is combined with which protein, so that at some stage between condensation reactions we must include some sort of acyl transfer.

If, as present evidence seems to imply (7), the substrates for the reactions which intervene between condensation steps are the carrier protein derivatives (not the enzyme derivatives), then the overall sequence in fatty-acid synthesis would appear to be

$$\text{acyl-CP} + \text{enzyme} \longrightarrow \text{acyl-enzyme}$$
$$\text{acyl-enzyme} + \text{malonyl-CP} \longrightarrow (\text{reaction complex})$$
$$\longrightarrow \text{acylacetyl-CP} + \text{enzyme} + CO_2$$
$$\text{acylacetyl-CP} \xrightarrow{\text{steps}} \text{higher acyl-CP}$$

Such a sequence offers immediate difficulties if we seek to use it directly for polyketoacyl assembly, since the growing assembly must be passed to and fro, between enzyme and carrier protein, in a manner hardly befitting a labile molecule.

However, the involvement of a chelating metal again simplifies the problem. The catalytic mechanism of the condensation reaction is inherently likely to involve a chelating metal, which can promote the necessary proximity of the reacting centers and also, by its electropositive character, facilitate the decarboxylation and enhance the electrophilic character of the acyl carbon. In Figure 2.11 I have suggested a mechanism for the reaction, in which the condensing enzyme carries a single —SH group and a metal ion. The thioacyl derivative of the enzyme is formed first, and this then accepts, by further coordination with the metal, the malonyl-CP (here written as the enol). Condensation-decarboxylation occurs within the com-

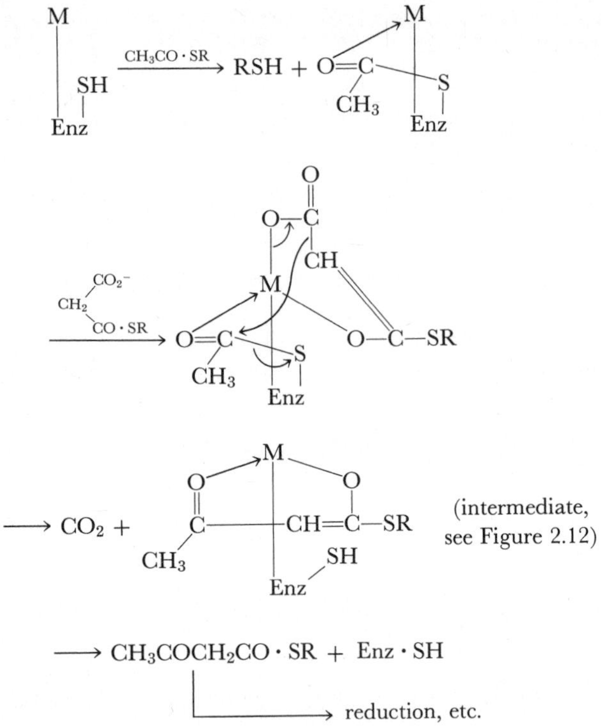

Figure 2.11.   Possible involvement of a metal in the condensation reaction of fatty-acid synthesis (RSH = acyl carrier protein).

plex, producing the acylacetyl product attached to the carrier protein by the thioester link of the original malonyl-CP, but still attached to the enzyme through the metal. The construction of models shows that all the stereoelectronic requirements for this concerted reaction can be met. For fatty-acid synthesis, we now postulate dissociation of this complex to give acylacetyl-CP from which the higher acyl-CP is generated, by reduction, etc.

For polyketide synthesis, however, we do not need the reduction steps and it is desirable to retain the chelation so as to stabilize subsequent intermediates. In Figure 2.12, therefore, I have supposed that the acylacetyl-CP–metal–thiolenzyme complex of Figure 2.11 undergoes transacylation internally, giving the acylacetyl-derivative of the enzyme, and that this reacts again, as shown, with further molecules of malonyl-CP. Each condensation is followed by the internal transacylation, and each condensation effectively *inserts* a (CH_2CO) group between the growing chain and the enzyme. When a certain stage is reached, this growing loop of $(CH_2CO)_n$ units itself becomes capable of occupying the coordination positions of the metal ion; in the simplest case this is attained with four C_2 units, and the resultant complex is of the type we have already discussed, illustrated in Figure 2.9. Once again, the stereochemical requirements of all these reactions are very elegantly met in models.

8. Conclusions

This is, I believe, about as far as we can—or should—go in our reasoning. Possibly, from some of the clues so far given, and from existing evidence on the trace-metal requirements of certain fungi, we might be able to predict the identity of the "metal ion" whose geometry and chemistry appear to be so convenient. Ultimately, extensions to more complex polyketides might legitimately be described. But for the immediate future we must be content to wait until the *sine qua non* of ideal biochemistry has been attained—a purified enzyme. Since, at present, even a crude cell-free extract capable of the synthesis of a polyketide is a rare phenomenon, our wait may be a long one. However, it may be shorter if a few more biochemists realize that here is a problem of respectable dimensions.

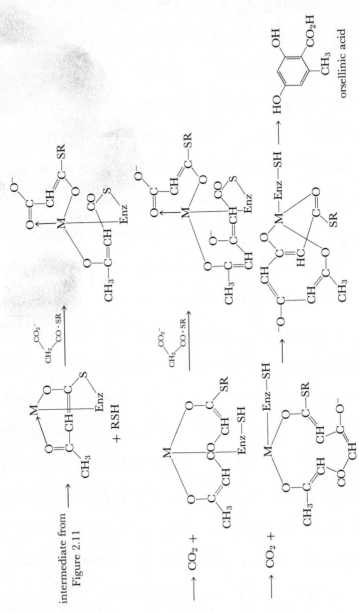

Figure 2.12. Suggested mechanism for formation of the enzyme-bound, metal-stabilized, polyketide "loop."

40

REFERENCES

1. Birch, A. J., and F. W. Donovan, *Australian J. Chem.,* **6,** 360 (1953).
2. Birch, A. J., *Fortschr. Chem. Org. Naturstoffe,* **14,** 186 (1957).
3. Bentley, R., *Ann. Rev. Biochem.,* **31,** 589 (1962).
4. Neish, A. C., in J. H. Harborn (ed.) *Biochemistry of Phenolic Compounds,* (Academic Press, London, 1964), p. 295.
5. Mosbach, K., *Acta Chem. Scand.,* **14,** 457 (1960).
6. McCormick, J. R. D., in Z. Vanek and Z. Hostalek (ed.), *Biogenesis of Antibiotic Substances* (Czechoslovak Academy of Sciences, Prague, 1965) p. 73.
7. Vagelos, R., *Ann. Rev. Biochem.,* **33,** 139 (1964).
8. Birch, A. J., R. A. Massy-Westropp, and C. J. Moye, *Australian J. Chem.,* **8,** 539 (1955).
9. Bassett, E. W., and S. W. Tanenbaum, *Biochem. Biophys. Acta,* **40,** 535 (1960).
10. Bentley, R., and J. G. Keil, *Proc. Chem. Soc.,* 111 (1961).
11. Bu'Lock, J. D., and H. M. Smalley, *Proc. Chem. Soc.,* 209 (1961).
12. Bu'Lock, J. D., H. M. Smalley, and G. N. Smith, *J. Biol. Chem.,* **237,** 1778 (1962).
13. Holker, J. S. E., J. Staunton, and W. B. Whalley, *J. Chem. Soc.,* 16 (1964).
14. Mosbach, K., *Acta Chem. Scand.,* **18,** 1591 (1964).
15. *Cf.* Corcoran, J. W., in Z. Vanek and Z. Hostalek (ed.), *Biogenesis of Antibiotic Substances* (Czechoslovak Academy of Sciences, Prague 1965) p. 131.
16. Gatenbeck, S., and K. Mosbach, *Acta Chem. Scand.,* **13,** 1561 (1959).
17. Lynen, F., and M. Tada, *Angew. Chem.,* **73,** 513 (1961).
18. Brodie, J. D., G. Wasson, and J. W. Porter, *J. Biol. Chem.,* **239,** 1346 (1964).
19. Allport, D. C., and J. D. Bu'Lock, *J. Chem. Soc.,* 654 (1960).
20. Fleming, I., and J. Harley-Mason, *Proc. Chem. Soc.,* 245 (1961).
21. Cymerman-Craig, J., and M. Moyle, *Proc. Chem. Soc.,* 149 (1962).

3

THE REGULATION OF SECONDARY BIOSYNTHESIS

Biochemistry has progressed from the identification of cell components *via* an understanding of cell reactions towards the investigation of cellular control mechanisms, so that at the present time most would agree that it is the collective regulation of individual enzymic activities that makes organic life possible. Inevitably, these most recent developments have given priority to the study of control mechanism in primary metabolism, in which the key processes of classical biochemistry are comprised. However, we have already seen how the study of secondary metabolism has undergone a similar evolution, from the isolation and recognition of "natural products," *via* the study of their biosynthesis, and hence again towards the study of control mechanisms. These control mechanisms, indeed, ultimately describe the key distinction between primary and secondary metabolic processes; they also have their practical importance, when (as so often occurs in industrial fermentations) the organism's own controls seem just out of access to the chemical engineer. Nowhere has the study of control mechanisms in secondary metabolism attained the level of sophistication professed by molecular biologists regarding *E. coli,* but there has accumulated an interesting body of evidence, direct and indirect. Today, by considering some of this evidence, I hope to show, at least, that regulation of secondary metabolism occurs, and that it involves mechanisms already familiar.

1. Control by Limiting Precursors

The chemist's interpretation of secondary metabolite structures has provided us with the first data on the problem of controls. It is conceivable that primary and secondary processes can be linked by the involvement of enzymes in common, though in view of the lower substrate-specificities which secondary biosynthesis often displays, this may seem unlikely. There will be important linkages through the common use of such reagents as ATP, $NADPH_2$, etc., and consequently, a degree of control and interaction like that which these reagents supply within the system of primary metabolism. Of particular importance, however, are the connections which are implicit (1) in the identification of the "precursors" of secondary metabolites, i.e., of the intermediates in primary metabolism which are the peculiar substrates for the special secondary biosynthesis. Once these precursors are identified, a number of regulatory phenomena are immediately recognizable.

To take a well-known example, consider the case of benzyl-penicillin (Figure 3.1). Structural features and precursor-incorporation experiments identify directly the roles of cysteine, valine, and phenylacetic acid. From this it follows that any events in primary metabolism which influence the availability of these precursors will correspondingly influence the synthesis of benzylpenicillin. For example, the availability of the aminoacids will be influenced by the competition of protein synthesis, and—except in strains with defective feedback—by the normal control these aminoacids exert upon their own biosynthesis. However, there are two important qualifica-

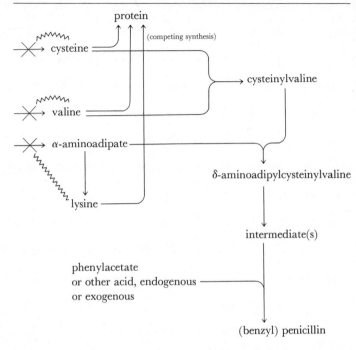

Figure 3.1. Precursor requirements which can limit the synthesis of benzylpenicillin. ⋀⋀⋀ ✕ indicates an inhibitory feedback effect.

tions to such a simple picture. Once the supply of any substrate exceeds a certain level, the reaction will cease to be substrate-limited and become enzyme-limited. This kind of limit represents, therefore, an "intrinsic capacity" for carrying out a reaction that will be independent of all manipulations designed to increase substrate availability. A second qualification arises from the lower substrate-specificity of many of the steps in secondary biosynthesis. Thus, in the synthesis of penicillins, the final acylation step is not very specific, so that a wide range of acids can be used similarly to phenylacetic acid.

Phenylacetic acid, therefore, can only be limiting for the particular synthesis of benzylpenicillin, not for the whole process of penicillin formation. This point appears even more strikingly in the case of other oligopeptide antibiotics, when the nonspecific step is not the last in the sequence. Thus, in the actinomycins, any of several aminoacids can be incorporated into the middle of the peptide chains (2), and none can uniquely limit the overall synthesis.

Within limits of this kind, however, a substantial part of what is known about the dynamics of penicillin formation, and likewise of other secondary metabolites, can be understood in terms of regulation by limiting precursor supply. In the particular case of the penicillins, the recent discovery by Abraham and coworkers (3) of the part played by α-aminoadipic acid and the tripeptide δ-aminoadipyl-cysteinyl-valine, offers an interesting extension, since several older observations are now explicable. Since α-aminoadipate is a normal intermediate in lysine biosynthesis, we can now understand how the feedback effect of lysine can depress penicillin synthesis, and why certain lysine-dependent auxotrophs of *P. chrysogenum* show an impairment of penicillin production (Figure 3.1). To all of these requirements for penicillin synthesis we must, of course, add the requirement for the necessary activation reactions—whose nature is largely unknown. These will depend critically, for example, on the supply of ATP, and such "energy requirements" may well explain the beneficial effects of such materials as fatty acids, which do not seem entirely explicable in terms of the supply of direct precursors.

2. Metabolic Development in Fermentations

In discussing secondary biosynthesis, it is important to remember that it is not an invariable activity of the organism. It is characteristic of secondary metabolism that it is peculiar to certain conditions and stages of development, and therefore its controls must reflect both the immediate environment and the previous history of the organism. For an exceptional group of microbial products the term "growth-linked" has been coined, emphasizing that typical secondary metabolites are, in some way less easy to define, *not* produced in parallel with the "growth" of the organism.

Unfortunately, this commonly used term "growth" is a portmanteau word which is not always easy to define or to relate to what is usually measured. Even the bacteriologist has to distinguish between cell counts, viable-cell counts, and cell weights; but consider filamentous organisms—possibly aseptate and multinuclear—with varying "inclusions" and cell-walls which vary in thickness and often outlast their contents, etc. Only the fact that "growth" is not measured by typical experimental parameters such as dry weight is really clear. Most mycelial cultures have the further disadvantage of heterogeneity, with "young," "old," and "dead" cells present simultaneously. In surface cultures the environmental heterogeneity is also obvious, but even in the most carefully controlled submerged cultures, homogeneity of development and micro-environment is only approximate. Thus we cannot easily observe either "growth" or "development"—yet, to anyone who has worked in the field, it is quite apparent that these imponderables are somehow linked with the circumstances under which secondary metabolism manifests itself.

Much of our own work in this field* has been an attempt to explore and resolve this situation; we have been encouraged by other notable publications on similar topics which I shall refer to. We can begin by looking at a well-known situation typified in Figure 3.2, which represents (say) the production of fat by a yeast. We note that the dry weight of the yeast follows a smooth

* Carried out mainly by D. Hamilton, A. J. Powell, D. Shepherd, and H. M. Smalley.

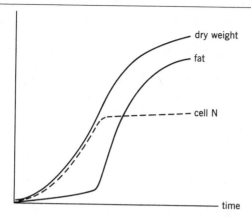

Figure 3.2.   Special biosynthesis—in this case accelerated lipid formation—following nitrogen exhaustion, at a time not defined by the dry weight curve.

sigmoid curve, yet the first part of this simple "growth" is accompanied by a low rate of fat synthesis and the second part by a rapid synthesis. In short, there are two qualitatively different kinds of "growth" concealed in the mathematically simple sigmoid. When we notice that the second kind of "growth" occurs after the nitrogen of the medium is exhausted, and indeed involves no net protein synthesis, we realize that (in terms a bacteriologist would accept) it cannot really be termed "growth" at all. And if true growth is "what occurs during the first part of the experiment," we will be content to say that the rapid synthesis of fat, which is a secondary metabolic phenomenon, occurs *after* growth has ended.

This kind of approach is given far greater refinement in the work of Borrow et al. (4) on *Gibberella fujikuroi*. Using defined synthetic media, these authors were able to define experimentally a phase of "balanced" replicatory growth, in which all the nutrients are taken up in an unchanging ratio, and which is therefore terminated when any single nutrient is exhausted.

In this phase the gross composition of the mycelium remains uniform. Subsequent events depend on the balance of remaining nutrients, but in general (providing the carbon source is not exhausted), the later "unbalanced" growth is marked by nonreplicatory assimilation, and, in particular, by secondary metabolic reactions such as accelerated lipid synthesis and the formation of gibberellins.

The principles of this work seem to be of general validity, but the ideal of truly balanced growth as the continued exact replication of the inoculum is seldom, if ever, observed in detail. More commonly, the earlier phase is also one of a steadily increasing imbalance, such as the growth of the aminoacid pool discussed later, but here we should note Taber's different characterization based on a study of *Claviceps* fermentations (5). Using phosphate as the exhaustible nutrient, and defining "growth" in terms of polymeric nonextractable mycelial residues (experimentally convenient), Taber distinguishes a phase of true replication, followed by a phase in which "primary shunt-products" such as polyols and oligosaccharides accumulate, followed by a phase in which true secondary metabolites like the ergot alkaloids are formed.

Generally, I believe that the truth lies somewhere between these two views, and that the "growth phase" prior to secondary metabolite formation is not quite so uniform as Borrow et al. imply, nor yet so sharply divisible as Taber's classification suggests. However, before describing some of our own studies, it is worth noting another, rather different, contribution. Most successful laboratory work in this field has been carried out with cultures which have been carefully tended so that they will develop as uniformly and homogeneously as possible. The conditions of industrial fermentations are often fundamentally different, and sharply phased development is seldom observed. Nevertheless, development similar to that in well-phased fermentations does occur. This has been abundantly demonstrated by the work of Becker (6), who applied, not the batch-measurements that are normally used, but cytochemical and morphological criteria of phasing which can be applied to individual mycelial aggregates in a population. Her work shows quite clearly that, in several industrial-type "smooth" fermentations, developmental changes similar to those in "homogeneous" cultures occur, but they spread through the population rapidly or slowly according to the culture conditions.

3. Trophophase and Idiophase

Penicillium urticae is a tolerably well-behaved fungus which we first used for investigations of polyketide synthesis and metabolism, and have since used it as our private equivalent of *E. coli*, i.e., as a basis for sweeping generalizations. To describe its behavior in well-phased submerged cultures we introduced (7) the terms "trophophase" and "idiophase." The trophophase is roughly equivalent to the concept of "balanced growth" used by Borrow et al., but avoids any implication that the inoculum is exactly replicated. The idiophase is the period when idiosyncratic (i.e., species-peculiar) secondary metabolites are produced.

Table One presents some of the gross differences which we have found in *P. urticae* between trophophase and idiophase cultures. This general picture agrees with the situations described by Borrow et al. and by Taber, and indeed with many other data for a wide range of fermentations now described in the literature, without adding much to our understanding. These are merely some of the criteria upon which the distinction of phases can be based.

For more insight into the differences underlying Table One, we turned to respirometric studies, and in particular, to the radiorespirometric technique of Cheldelin et al. (8), which we modified so as to permit continuous simultaneous measure-

TABLE 1
Differences between trophophase and idiophase in *P. urticae*.

	Rate of dry wt. increase	Glucose uptake	N and P uptake	Mycelial SH %	Mycelial RNA %	Mycelial lipids %	Free amino-N %	Keto-acids %	Phenols
Trophophase (transition)	rising	rapid	rapid	high maximal	high maximal	low	high falling	—	absent first
Idiophase	falling	cont'd	none	low	low	high	low	maximal	diverse

ments of $^{14}CO_2$ evolution from pairs of substrates (e.g., 1-^{14}C- and 2-^{14}C-acetate). We made series of such measurements (7), using mycelium from different stages in the *P. urticae* fermentation, and Figures 3.3–3.6 show some typical results. For example, the data for U-^{14}C-glucose give a ready measurement of the Q_{CO_2} which can be confirmed more arduously by conventional techniques. Figure 3.3 shows that there is a high respiratory activity in the trophophase and moderate activity in the idiophase, with a minimum at the transition. The data for 1-^{14}C-acetate are similar. However, when we combine these with the data for 1- and 6-^{14}C-glucose and 2-^{14}C-acetate respectively, further details emerge.

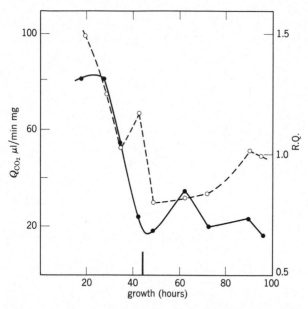

Figure 3.3.   R. Q. (broken line) and Q_{CO_2} (full line) measured by Warburg technique on *P. urticae* culture samples of increasing age; vertical bar marks onset of idiophase (7).

The method of calculation of the relative importance of alternative pathways of hexose catabolism from radiorespirometric data has been widely applied and seriously criticized; generally, I am on the side of the appliers. In our own work we have not sought precise quantitative results but the demonstration of qualitative effects, and we find that the qualitative conclusions are not very sensitive to the method of calculation that is used. For the record, the method of Wang et al. (8) was used for the data in Figure 3.5, which shows the relative contributions of the hexose monophosphate and glycolytic pathways. It is worth noting that a similar picture for *P. chrysogenum* was presented by Heath and Koffler (9), with the hexose monophosphate pathway being of greatest relative importance in young mycelium prior to penicillin production.

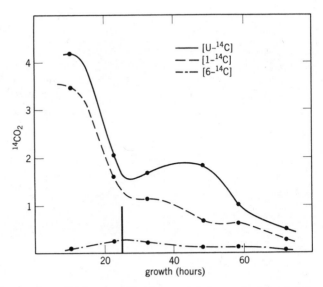

Figure 3.4. $^{14}CO_2$ released in 2-hour periods from variously labeled glucose by *P. urticae* mycelium of increasing age; vertical bar marks onset of idiophase (7).

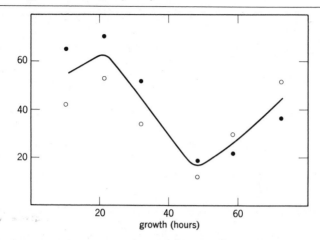

Figure 3.5.   Percentage of glucose metabolized by hexose monophosphate pathway, by mycelium of *P. urticae* of different ages (7).

The tricarboxylic-acid cycle functions both as a pathway for the phosphorylative oxidation of acetyl-CoA, and as a source of synthetic intermediates (such as α-ketoglutarate). These two functions are to some extent opposed, and from the relative contributions of 1- and 2-^{14}C-acetate to the respiratory $^{14}CO_2$, it is possible to calculate their relative importance. A simple treatment of the necessary calculation has been given by Strisower et al. (10), and this method has been used for the data in Figure 3.6, but again it is possible to show that more refined methods of calculation give essentially the same qualitative answer. The result obtained is a striking one—the proportion of cycle intermediates being withdrawn is very high both in the trophophase, when the overall rate of acetate oxidation is high, and in the full idiophase when the overall rate is low, but during the trophophase-idiophase transition when the overall rate is minimal, this diversion of intermediates is extremely low and the cycle is almost entirely devoted to oxidation.

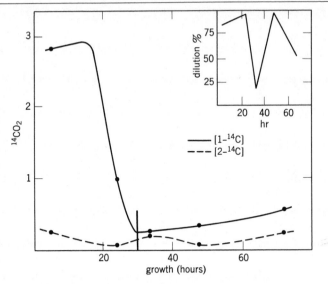

Figure 3.6. $^{14}CO_2$ released in 2-hour periods from [1-^{14}C]- and [2-^{14}C]-acetate by *P. urticae* culture samples of increasing age; vertical bar marks onset of idiophase. Inset: percentage dilution in tricarboxylic acid cycle (7).

An interpretation of these respiratory events is facilitated by the work of Bent and Morton (11), who investigated the aminoacid pool of *P. griseofulvum* under conditions of nitrogen exhaustion. Since *P. urticae* is virtually the same organism, we did no more than confirm the general trend of their results for our own material. During the trophophase the mycelium accumulates a large pool of α-aminoacids, in which glutamic acid, glutamine, and alanine are particularly important. Following nitrogen exhaustion these particular acids, i.e., the ones most closely related to tricarboxylic-acid cycle intermediates, show a very rapid decline. (It is interesting to note that typical idiophase characteristics are shown in Bent and Morton's data on the oligopeptides of *P. griseofulvum,* which show a marked *increase* at this time and are thus functionally analogous to the oligopeptides of *P. chrysogenum*.) As one would expect from these observations, we have found that as the α-aminoacid pool is depleted, the α-ketoacid pool increases. Curiously, this increase is mainly in pyruvate, rather than in α-ketoglutarate, the level of which seems to be fairly well regulated (Figure 3.7).

The balance between the tricarboxylic-acid cycle α-ketoacids and the transaminating α-aminoacids is a step of fundamental importance in the assimilation of nitrogen into protein, and it also represents a major utilization of reduced coenzymes provided by the hexose monophosphate shunt and similar reactions. Thus, it is in this region of the metabolic network that the consequences of nutritional limitations, which end replicatory protein-synthesis in the trophophase, have their sharpest impact. Probably the decline in hexose mono-

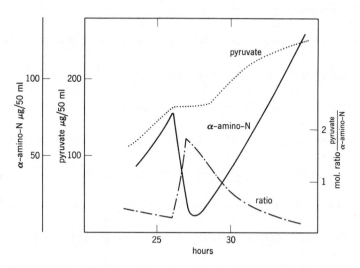

Figure 3.7. Variations of total α-amino-N and of pyruvate in cultures of *P. urticae* (7).

phosphate oxidation represents a later adjustment to the new situation. It is also likely that the disturbances in and around the tricarboxylic-acid cycle are the perturbing phenomena which lead to the production of secondary metabolites.

We believe that these phenomena are of rather general significance. Gatenbeck (12) has indicated that similar respiratory events may occur in *Penicillium islandicum* when nitrogen exhaustion is accompanied by the appearance of anthraquinones, while Windisch and Bronn (13) have described in *Claviceps purpurea* a situation in which a sharp decline from a high level of respiration leads to efficient synthesis of ergot alkaloids. Possibly this type of situation underlies even more complex phenomena than secondary biosynthesis. Hawker (14) has detected similar respiratory events prior to sporulation in *Rhizopus* sp., while the metabolic site deduced from our own results is virtually identical with that identified by Cantino (15) as the site which determines the differentiation pathway in *Blastocladiella*.

For the specific problem of secondary metabolite formation, however, we must ask how these sudden disturbances of the primary metabolic network can cause the opening up of synthetic pathways leading to new products. It seems to me that there are two mechanisms to be considered, though these are not necessarily exclusive. It is conceivable that the enzymes requisite for secondary biosynthesis are already present, but are virtually inoperative because of the low levels of their proper substrates. Increases in the levels of limiting substrates and the elimination of competing reactions would allow secondary biosynthesis to proceed. Alternatively, the enzymes initiating the secondary metabolic sequence could be synthesized *de novo* at this time by derepression under the action of substrates which hitherto had been present at too low a level to act as inducers.

Superficially, either type of explanation will fit the present data. The fact that, even in very carefully phased cultures, some secondary biosyntheses often seem to occur, even at a very low rate, could be due either to incomplete competition of primary metabolism with constitutive enzymes of secondary biosynthesis, or to a low level of gratuitous derepression of inducible enzymes. In the next section I hope to show that derepression plays a part, along with feedback mechanisms, in secondary metabolism, but at the present time it would be premature to think of such mechanisms as the only explanation of the relationship between "growth" and secondary biosynthesis. In *Neurospora*, tyrosinase (which must surely be classed as an enzyme of secondary metabolism since it can be assigned no certain primary role) is inducible and can appear in a manner appropriately related to growth and development (16); equally, the intracellular proteinases of *P. griseofulvum* appear as a result of *de novo* synthesis following nitrogen exhaustion (17). On the other hand, accelerated lipid synthesis, which is a typical secondary metabolic activity, seems more likely to be due to the release of a preformed system from substrate-limited conditions. However, either type of interpretation provides us with a satisfactory explanation of another feature of secondary metabolism, which I have not mentioned. The great variety of secondary metabolites now known derives from a surprisingly limited selection of precursors (malonyl-CoA, mevalonic acid, etc.) (1); these precursors are also key intermediates in primary biosynthesis, and in general they are themselves produced by reactions whose rate normally controls a whole biosynthetic sequence, so that in general, in the undisturbed operation of primary metabolism, they are present in minimal amounts. It is precisely such substrates, therefore, that will most easily restrict the operation of a preformed secondary biosynthetic enzyme, or fail to derepress the synthesis of an inducible one, until the intervention of circumstances similar to those described here. For example, there is evidence that mevalonic acid plays a controlling role of this kind in the synthesis of gibberellins (18), and likewise, tryptophan, in the synthesis of ergot alkaloids (19).

4. Secondary Metabolic Sequences

A few secondary metabolites, such as itaconic acid, arise by the action of just one novel enzyme, but the majority are produced by a series of reaction steps, and though these may be less well regulated than similar sequences in primary metabolism, interactions and some degree of control do occur and can be usefully investigated. When the secondary metabolites of an organism are investigated in detail—i.e., when chemical studies are taken beyond an examination of the most easily isolated product—it is common to find that whole groups of substances of obvious biogenetic relationship occur together. The details of the sequences in which these are formed are often difficult to disentangle, and this is at least in part an effect of the lower specificity of some of the enzymic steps. This results in situations in which the sequence of reactions leading from one substance to another can be varied, so that more than one pathway, and more than one set of intermediates, can exist. Such a situation is exemplified in the phenolic metabolites of *P. urticae*, as shown in Figure 3.8, largely based on the work of Tanenbaum and Bassett (20).

Here, as in many systems of this kind, there is one reaction that defines the whole group of products eventually obtained, and stands first in the whole sequence. This key reaction is the synthesis of 6-methylsalicylic acid, the parent compound of the entire series. In other Penicillia the synthesis of orsellenic acid plays a similar key role. Now, it is curious that when we seek to define these key reactions for various systems, we find that the products, the various "parent compounds," are not, in general, well known as natural products, although they are often

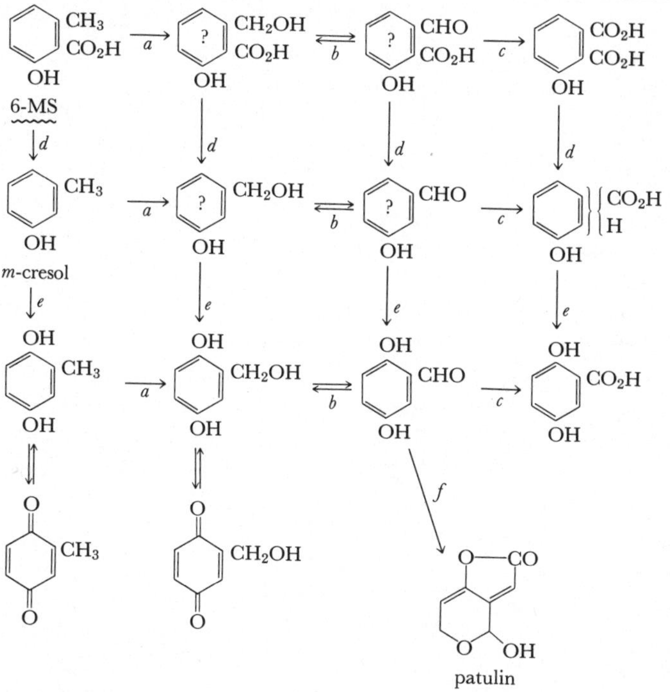

Figure 3.8. The further metabolites of 6-MS in *P. urticae* (7); note that six reactions (*a-f*) suffice to afford 16 metabolites, of which all but 4 (shown with queries) are now demonstrated. The substrate for reaction (*f*) is probably, but not certainly, gentisaldehyde.

the simplest of a series. On close examination, these parent compounds may be found to have fairly widespread occurrence but only exceptionally do they accumulate in any large amount. Usually they are subjected to further metabolism, whether this is simple alkylation or esterification, or a more complex series of relatively drastic reactions. Thus, in most strains of *P. urticae,* etc., 6-methylsalicylic acid only accumulates transiently (Figure 3.9). In the last section I considered some of the evidence as to how the biosynthesis of these parent metabolites becomes operative at the beginning of tropho-phase conditions; here I would like to examine the ensuing reactions, in which the pattern of secondary metabolism becomes diversified.

In well-synchronized cultures of *P. urticae* (Figure 3.9) there is a detectable period in which 6-methylsalicylic acid alone is formed, after which the gentisyl derivatives (*cf.* Figure 3.8) appear, followed by patulin. These observations are based on spectroscopic and chromatographic assays. Similarly, in labeling experiments using similar cultures supplied with ^{14}C-acetate or -malonate, it is clear that the initial synthesis of 6-methylsalicylate is not complicated by further reactions,

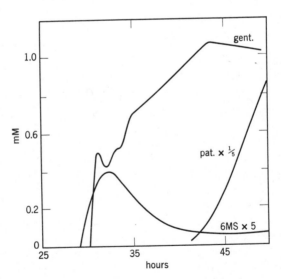

Figure 3.9.   Variation of 6-MS, gentisyl derivatives, and patulin in a typical *P. urticae* fermentation (7).

whereas at a later stage 6-methylsalicylate is merely an intermediate. Moreover, if 6-methylsalicylic acid is added to
trophophase mycelium, it is not converted into the gentisyl
derivatives or into patulin, at least not until an appreciable
time has elapsed. It looks as though the enzymes responsible
for the further metabolism of 6-methylsalicylic acid are either
absent or inactive until the organism has been exposed to
6-methylsalicylic acid for an appreciable time.

This view was confirmed when *P. urticae* was grown in continuous culture. At a dilution rate approximately adjusted to
match the growth rate in the trophophase, we found it possible to maintain *P. urticae* indefinitely in a state where no
6-methylsalicylate was produced, provided, of course, that
throughput was begun during the trophophase. However, if
the dilution were not started until the end of the trophophase,
i.e., by commencing throughput (at a somewhat lower rate)
when 6-methylsalicylate first appeared, the cultures would
continue to synthesize 6-methylsalicylate without ever beginning to convert this into gentisyl derivatives or patulin. If
dilution were then halted for a few hours, the full idiophase
pattern of patulin formation would be established. We also
observed that in cultures which had been suspended in the
stage of 6-methylsalicylate synthesis without conversion to
gentisyl derivatives, a quantity of *m*-cresol was produced. This
implies decarboxylation of 6-methylsalicylate (see Figure 3.8).
Normally this is not an important reaction, but decarboxylation of the oxidized derivatives of 6-methylsalicylate is a step
in the full sequence to the gentisyl derivatives.

We interpret these observations (7) as indicating that at least
some of the enzymes involved in the oxidation of 6-methyl-
salicylate are induced sequentially following the first synthesis
of 6-methylsalicylate; this, or some simple derivative, being the
inducer. Other enzymes, like the decarboxylase, are perhaps
constitutive, or possibly the decarboxylase is induced by a

lower concentration of 6-methylsalicylate than is required for the oxidation enzymes.

Once again, we do not pretend that these results are unique. There are indications in the literature that similar effects occur in other secondary biosynthetic sequences, and I believe that the exploration of these sequences specifically in terms of this kind of mechanism will be fruitful. As I have already pointed out, it is rather unusual to find an organism that contents itself with a single special reaction leading without elaboration to a single secondary metabolite. It occurred to us that the more general situation, in which the products are diversified by subsequent reactions of the parent metabolite, might in a sense be functional. So far as I can see, the main function of secondary metabolism is discharged by the biosynthetic process itself, rather than by the product, and that being so, the diversification reactions might have the function of removing the product. This would be desirable if the product were toxic or, more generally, if it were capable of regulating its own synthesis by a negative-feedback mechanism. *A priori,* it also seemed that reactions such as polyketide synthesis or polyisoprenoid folding, in which specific matrices for structures resembling the reaction product must be involved, might be particularly susceptible to end-product inhibition. Certain recorded observations might be explicable in these terms, and such considerations led us to examine the effects of 6-methylsalicylic acid upon the organism which produces it.

We found that these effects are surprisingly complex, and before they could be sorted out we had to make long series of experiments which were usually quite unsatisfactory. Here I shall merely outline the eventual state of our findings.

First of all, we discovered that when 6-methylsalicylate in concentrations of $10^{-3} \sim 10^{-4}$ M is added to *P. urticae,* it is taken up in a very odd manner. The acid is removed from the medium very rapidly, but after a period varying between five minutes and one hour, the acid reappears in the medium (Figure 3.10). This occurs with trophophase and idiophase mycelium, irrespective of the capacity to synthesize 6-methylsalicylate *de novo*, and the picture is only modified with late idiophase mycelium capable of rapid conversion into patulin. Possibly this effect is due to a change in the internal pH of the cells—it does not occur with dead mycelium—but whatever its mechanism it complicates experiments in which 6-methylsalicylate levels are to be measured!

Tanenbaum and Bassett, using surface cultures, obtained results which suggested to them that 6-methylsalicylate inhibited patulin synthesis (20). Similarly, we found that the addition of extra 6-methylsalicylate to patulin-producing cultures had little or no effect on the yield of patulin, although

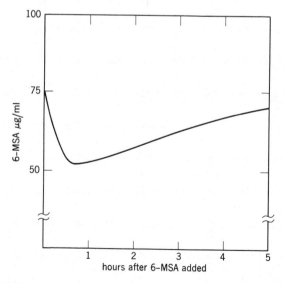

Figure 3.10. Concentration of 6-methylsalicylic acid in the aqueous phase following addition to a suspension of *P. urticae* mycelium.

labeled 6-methylsalicylate was undoubtedly being converted into patulin. We decided to measure *de novo* synthesis by the incorporation of ^{14}C-acetate into 6-methylsalicylate, in cultures to which 6-methylsalicylate had been added, and were gratified to find a marked inhibition of this incorporation by $2 \sim 6 \times 10^{-4}$ M 6-methylsalicylate. We then found that at these concentrations there was an equally effective inhibition of incorporation of the ^{14}C into lipids, into mycelial insolubles, and into respired CO_2. Moreover, there was a similar inhibition when the ^{14}C was supplied as glucose; indeed, the total production of CO_2 and the increase in total mycelial weight were also strongly inhibited. In short, all these effects were due to a general inhibition of all metabolic processes, by some fundamental toxicity of the 6-methylsalicylate, interesting in itself, but not the type of effect we sought to detect. The same effects were shown by other salicylates in the same concentration range, and indeed, we should have expected this.

At lower concentrations, $0.5 \sim 2 \times 10^{-4}$ M, these general effects are less marked or absent, and only in this range did 6-methylsalicylate behave differently from, for example, the isomeric 3-methylsalicylate. In particular, when ^{14}C-labeled 6-methylsalicylate was added at these concentrations to idiophase mycelium, it was recovered after several hours with its specific activity unchanged, but without producing any general effect upon the metabolic activity of the mycelium. This suggests that this concentration was able to inhibit the synthesis of 6-methylsalicylic acid selectively. The concentrations used are about the same as those normally attained by endogenous 6-methylsalicylate in control cultures, and it appears that these are sufficient to exercise a specific feedback effect upon 6-methylsalicylate synthesis. The ability to convert 6-methylsalicylate into a variety of less inhibitory substances could therefore be functional in the sense of allowing 6-methylsalicylate synthesis to proceed.

Conclusions

I do not believe that *P. urticae* is in any way unique, nor indeed am I certain that it has been the best organism with which to explore all the levels of control that we have tried to investigate. At various points I have indicated parallel or clearer effects in other biosynthetic sequences. Here, however, I shall try to summarize what we believe to be the controlling mechanisms in this particular case of a secondary biosynthetic system.

The primary metabolic pathways of *P. urticae* are intrinsically adjusted to the trophophase function of growth, by (approximate) replication. Exhaustion of specific nutrients, or possibly an inherent over-production of specific cell components, leads ultimately to the dislocation of this adjustment. During the dislocation, certain key intermediates, hitherto limiting, attain unusually high levels. The secondary biosynthetic systems then become operative, either as a result of new enzyme synthesis, induced by these intermediates, or by the action of enzymes already present but hitherto limited by the availability of the substrates, for which primary processes have been powerfully competing. Once the new biosynthetic process is established, it may be itself liable to product inhibition. Enzymes which remove the product, and thus permit continuation of the secondary process, may already be present, but others are produced *de novo* by derepression mechanisms. The product of the first secondary process is thereby diversified into a variety of metabolites.

Perhaps if *P. urticae* were really our *E. coli,* we could perform a few more experiments and then regard the whole problem of secondary metabolism as solved. But beyond this level of explanation there lies a further problem. Granted that, in terms such as I have outlined, we can explain the general pattern of secondary metabolism and its integration with primary processes, why should the detailed course of secondary metabolism vary so spectacularly from one organism to another when the primary processes are so similar? Secondary metabolites are an expression of the individuality of the species in molecular terms, and possibly these are the most appropriate terms in which that individuality can be expressed, since the "senses" of microorganisms are all chemical. By their fruits they shall be known . . . but the mycelium has no need of a microscope.

REFERENCES

1. Bu'Lock, J. D., *Advan. Appl. Microbiol.,* **3,** 293 (1961).
2. Katz, E., and W. A. Goss, *Biochem. J.,* **73,** 458 (1959).
3. Abraham, E. P., G. G. F. Newton, and S. C. Warren, in Z. Vanek and Z. Hostalek (ed.), *Biogenesis of Antibiotic Substances* (Czechoslovak Academy of Sciences, Prague, 1965), p. 169.
4. Borrow, A., E. G. Jefferys, R. H. J. Kessel, E. C. Lloyd, P. B. Lloyd, and I. S. Nixon, *Can. J. Microbiol.,* **7,** 227 (1961).
5. Taber, W. A., *Appl. Microbiol,* **12,** 321 (1964).
6. Becker, Z. E., *Mitt. Versuchssta. Garungsgewerbe, Inst. Angew. Mikrobiol. (Wien),* **18,** 1 (1964).
7. Bu'Lock, J. D., D. Hamilton, M. A. Hulme, A. J. Powell, D. Shepherd, H. M. Smalley, and G. N. Smith, *Can. J. Microbiol.,* **11,** 765 (1965).
8. Wang, C. H., I. Stern, C. M. Gilmour, S. Klungsoyr, D. J. Reed, J. J. Bialy, B. E. Christensen, and V. H. Cheldelin, *J. Bacteriol.,* **76,** 207 (1958).
9. Heath, E. C., and H. Koffler, *J. Bacteriol.,* **71,** 174 (1956).
10. Strisower, E. H., G. D. Kohler, and I. L. Chaikoff, *J. Biol. Chem.,* **198,** 115 (1952).
11. Bent, K. J., and A. G. Morton, *Biochem. J.,* **92,** 260 (1964).
12. Gatenbeck, S. in Z. Vanek and Z. Hostalek (ed.), *Biogenesis of Antibiotic Substances* (Czechoslovak Academy of Sciences, Prague, 1965), p. 255.
13. Windisch, S., and W. Bronn, U. S. Patent 2,936,266 (1960).
14. Hawker, L. E., and P. M. Hepden, *Ann. Botany (London),* **26,** 619 (1962).
15. Cantinoe, E. C., *Symp. Soc. Gen. Microbiol.,* **11,** 243 (1961).
16. Horowitz, H. N., M. Fling, H. L. MacLeod, and N. Sueka, *J. Mol. Biol.,* **2,** 96 (1960).

17. Morton, A. G., A. G. F. Dickerson, and D. J. F. England, *J. Exp. Bot.*, **11**, 116 (1960).
18. Birch, A. J., J. F. Grove, and I. S. Nixon, British Patent 844,341 (1959).
19. Floss, H. G., and U. Mothes, *Arch. Mikrobiol.*, **48**, 213 (1964).
20. Tanenbaum, S. W., and E. W. Bassett, *Biochim. Biophys. Acta*, **28**, 21 and 247 (1948); **40**, 535 (1960).

INDEX